Handbook for Clerks of Works

Handbook for Clerks of Works

Second edition

**Greater London Council
Department of Architecture
and Civic Design**

The Architectural Press. London

First published by the Greater London Council July 1973
Reprinted September 1973 and March 1974
Second edition published by the Architectural Press Ltd
1979
The Handbook was originally compiled by E. T. Dean,
formerly the Greater London Council Sites Manager
© Greater London Council 1973 and 1979
British Library Cataloguing in Publication Data
Greater London Council. Department of Architecture
  and Civic Design
  Handbook for Clerks of Works.—2nd ed.
  1. Building—England—London—Superintendence
  2. Greater London Council. Department of Architecture
  and Civic Design—Officials and employees
  I. Title
  624   TH438
  ISBN 0-85139-321-7
Printed in Great Britain by
W & J Mackay Ltd, Chatham

Contents

1 Duties and Responsibilities of a Clerk of Works

1 Generally

The architect-in-charge of the works is the group leader, who is charged with the whole responsibility for bringing the project to a satisfactory conclusion.
The group leader while retaining full responsibility for all aspects will usually delegate the individual job to a Job Architect who thereupon has, normally, a delegated responsibility for the day to day management of the job, for the quality of the work required and produced on site, for ensuring full compliance with all drawings, specifications and instructions, for co-ordination of the various elements of site supervision, and for setting the standards and quality of work required.
The resident Clerk of Works on site acts in direct assistance to the architect in these tasks and is responsible to him for all matters related to that site. While the Clerk of Works does not carry a legal responsibility under the contract, his responsibility being to the architect, he does occupy a position of considerable trust, and by the very fact of his engagement by the Department in the capacity of Clerk of Works, has an over-riding obligation to carry out his duties (on which outline guidance is given in this manual) in an efficient and dependable manner with the greatest of integrity throughout.
Very briefly the Clerk of Works function is:
1 To inspect in detail
2 To report concisely
3 To interpret clearly
4 To record completely
and by this means to carry out his part in the Job Architect/Clerk of Works team which has such an all important role in site supervision.

2 Definition of duties

For many years in the department, the Clerk of Works has been defined as:
' the representative of the Architect on site for the day-to-day detailed inspection of works in progress, to ensure that such works are executed in complete accordance with the contract documents and with the instructions issued from time to time by the architect-in-charge. He is to see that the specified standard of workmanship is maintained; that the materials used are of the specified quality; that construction throughout is sound; that the progress of the work accords with contract requirements, and that all essential facts relating to the work and the various stages of progress are properly recorded '.
In 1963, there having been previously no specific reference in the conditions of contract to the Clerk of

1

Works, a new edition of the RIBA Conditions of
Contract was published, and adopted by the Council.
Under Clause 10, agreed by the Joint Contracts Tribunal
on which the Council was represented, the Clerk of
Works was defined as:
'acting solely as an Inspector on behalf of the Employer
under the direction of the Architect . . .'

3   Effect of Clause 10

This provided in effect that a Clerk of Works cannot
himself issue instructions; directions via the Clerk of
Works become valid as instructed only if confirmed by
the Architect within two working days.
This did not define the term Inspector but of course the
Clerk of Works remained in the position as before of
being very much a key man in the contract, and the
Clerk of Works basic duties vis-a-vis the Architect as
before. It did however interpose some not inconsiderable
practical administrative difficulties in the confirmation
of every Clerk of Works Site Instruction by the Architect
within two working days of its issue.
It is extremely convenient in practice, and normally
expeditious, that instructions should be issued, by agreement between the architect-in-charge and the Clerk of
Works, to the Contractor via the Clerk of Works Site
Instruction form.

4   Definition of Clerk of Works duties in issue of instructions

To make this practicable, in fact to avoid the procedure
becoming completely unworkable, each Clerk of Works,
at new briefing, should ask his architect-in-charge to
define to the Contractor at the preliminary briefing
meeting the duties of the Clerk of Works, and have
the Contractor's agreement thereto.

5   Contractor's attitudes

Where the Contractor is one of some renown with
management staff fully experienced in local authority
work any adjustment is automatically made by the
Contractor's organisation to obtain the necessary
elasticity so that the contract can run smoothly.
In three or four cases, however, mainly small or medium
contractors operating with an uninformed contracts
manager, and an agent inexperienced in local government
work, where the Contractor's organisation try to work
pointedly to the letter of the contract (Clause 10),
considerable administrative, and often technical,
difficulties and frustrations have occurred with the whole
contract proceeding haltingly, and most uncomfortably,
for all concerned.
In the few cases such as this, where agreement on a
smooth procedure is difficult to obtain, there will, of
course, be no alternative but for the architect-in-charge

to lay on a special drill between himself, the Clerk of
Works and the Contractor's staff for confirmation within
the two working day period.

6 Specific limitations to Clerk of Works duties

A Clerk of Works should NOT
1 Give any direction whatever involving financial effect
without prior specific instruction from the architect-in-
charge.
2 Make any alteration to any basic detail of the contract
particulars without prior approval of the architect-in-
charge.
3 Approve the Contractor carrying out any remedial
measures that may involve any workmanship techniques
not approved beforehand.

7 Varieties of duties of a Clerk of Works

A Clerk of Works may be called upon to carry out a
variety of duties. He may work:
1 On contracts for new works of various sorts, controlled
by an architectural section of the department; and this
is the normal practice.
2 With an architect in private practice on new works
contracts.
3 On Modernisation and Conversion work, Rehabilitation
or Improvements and Maintenance.
4 On a ' Package Deal ' where the Architect, Consultants
and Control Staff are employed by the Contractor.
5 On temporary attachment to specialised groups in the
department, at County Hall; this may, for example,
include specialist piling work; the control of trial
boring contracts; assistance with training courses;
work on Ground Condition reports, and on foundation
records, in Site Manager's Section, Central Services.
It is essential that the Clerk of Works is at all times sure
of his position and authority, especially on ' Package
Deals ', and before taking over control of such a contract
he should discuss his position fully, with the Site
Manager in the case of the Housing Branch. In the case
of other branches of the department, or of the ILEA,
the Clerk of Works should discuss the position with his
appropriate Senior Officer, usually a Superintendent of
Works.

8 Knowledge of contract documents

In order to carry out his duties efficiently the Clerk of
Works must have a completely detailed knowledge of the
contract requirements. For this purpose, at an early
stage, he must thoroughly familiarise himself with:
1 The drawings—which he should know in full detail
and by which he must be able to check work.

2 The Specification—which may be a separate document for the older, or extension, contracts, or, in the case of the RIBA Local Authority Conditions of Contract now used in modified form by the Council will be incorporated in the Contract Bills as work section preambles.

3 Nominated Sub-contractors Specifications—with the relevant drawings. These should make clear the specified requirements upon which the nominated sub-contractor has been accepted.

4 The Bills of Quantities or, in the case of the new form of Contract, Contract Bills—a general understanding and a working knowledge of these Bills is essential.

5 The Conditions of Contract—and in particular the clauses in these Conditions relating to the Clerk of Works, and the issue of Site Instructions.

6 Work by other departments; for example Parks Department.

7 Work by other authorities: for example, Gas Board, Electricity Board, Local Borough GPO.

9 Building Regulations and Acts

The Building Regulations 1976, which came into operation from 31 January 1977, apply generally throughout England and Wales, with the exception of the Inner London Boroughs where the London Building Acts and Constructional By-laws continue to prevail. A Clerk of Works of the Greater London Council should be familiar with Building Regulations 1976, and with the London Building Acts and Constructional By-laws and the provisions in these Regulations and Acts which may apply to the contracts he is supervising.

10 Co-operative relations with Agent

While any departure from good practice or disregard of instructions must be handled speedily and firmly, and while the Site Agent (or General Foreman) must always be kept very much aware of the standard of quality the Clerk of Works requires, and intends to have, the establishment of good co-operative relations between Clerk of Works and Site Agent is an important factor in the successful execution of the contract.

It is expected that Clerks of Works, who necessarily must be men of judgment, should normally have little difficulty in establishing the appropriate co-operative relationships required between the Clerk of Works and the contractors staff.

11 Anticipation

During the course of the work the Clerk of Works should learn to sense probable sources of difficulty, and, in association with the Site Agent prevent such difficulty arising or overcome it as quickly as possible. Such foresight springs, in the main, from experience and from a full and detailed knowledge of the contract documents. Where instruction from the architect-in-charge would be necessary or a drawing is required, this is a matter where intelligent anticipation by the Clerk of Works is of great importance, and appropriate notification to the architect-in-charge would be invaluable.

12 Interpretation

The Clerk of Works must be able to interpret to the Contractor's staff, all phases of the work, all details from drawings, all specification clauses and all architect's or consultant's instructions of any kind.

13 Inspection

One of the most important points is for the Clerk of Works, by constant inspection, and quiet vigilance, to discover bad workmanship at its inception, before it gets established; he will in fact often be ahead of the agent in this, and while the Clerk of Works should avoid doing the agent's or general foreman's job for him, it is always a good tactical position to be in.

The Clerk of Works must inspect in detail, and check measure as necessary, every part of the work, and usually, as each day's work is carried out. It is strongly emphasised that a Clerk of Works is not doing his duty if he stands by and lets the contractor proceed to the completion of a faulty piece of work to have it condemned and pulled down. Where, as occasionally may happen, the contractor, woodenly it may seem, but often just trying it on to see how far he can go, proceeds with faulty work regardless of warnings this should be the subject of immediate written record, and report to the architect-in-charge.

14 Reporting

In the matter of report, as a routine, the Clerk of Works is to report back each week to the architect-in-charge, and verbally at all times that may be necessary and appropriate.

15 Recording and the Job Diary

The Job Diary is an important document for recording the day-to-day happenings on the job. Particularly of late years building contractors are using extensive documentation to support claims, some of which may be on flimsy ground or exaggerated, and it is essential that the Clerk of Works should keep quite a detailed diary.

16 Diary items

Amongst the items which should be noted in the Job Diary are:

1 Instructions:
   Any directions issued to contractor
   Verbal instructions or information given to Clerk
      of Works by architect

Verbal Instructions or information given by District
Surveyor or Structural Engineer
Decisions taken with officers of other departments.
2 Dayworks:
Reasons for taking items as dayworks
3 Weather:
Low temperatures
High winds
Rain or snow
4 Tests:
Records of tests made
5 Workmanship:
Any mention of bad workmanship to the contractor
or to any of his staff.
6 Delays:
Any delays that are evident, and the reasons for them,
in any specific operation, or between operations.
7 Drawings:
Any drawing, or information, that is needed or that
has been requested.
8 Concreting:
Concrete pouring, and striking of important items of
formwork, if not charted on the programme.
9 Labour:
Any labour problems including overtime bans, strikes,
troubles with labour-only gangs, etc.
10 Condemned Work:
Note of any condemned work, or any materials
that have been rejected, and details of all errors, pulling
down, cutting away, rebuilding or other remedial
measures that have had to be taken.
It should be routine for the Clerk of Works to write the
Job Diary up as soon as possible after events, and in
any case by the end of the day, so that memory is fresh.

17 Issue of Diary

Each Clerk of Works will be issued with a Personal
Diary, size three days per page, which he uses for his
personal records and retains.
In addition each contract will be issued with a Job
Diary, Dataday type A.4 sheet per day, which is to
remain on the contract and to be treated as one of the
Job documents in charge of and kept up by the Senior
Clerk of Works. This is not transferred with the Clerk of
Works.
If a Clerk of Works has more than one job of size he
is to have a Job Diary for each.

18 Query and Answer Book

The Clerk of Works is to keep a query and answer book
for each contract.
He is to record and date all queries raised by the
contractor and, similarly, record and date the answers
given by the architect, structural engineer or

consultants, etc., as the case may be.
The Clerk of Works should also record any queries that
he, himself, may raise with the architect, etc. and date
them and the answers in a similar manner.
This information will assist the architect with feed-back
and financial control when dealing with extensions
of time.

19 Weekly report—

The Clerk of Works is to make a Weekly Report on the
form provided, to be posted so as to reach the Department not later than noon on the Monday of each week,
in respect of the week ending on noon on the previous
Saturday. Two copies of the report should be sent to the
Department, and the Clerk of Works should retain a
further copy for himself for reference.

**20 Percentage completion
figures for housing**

The Weekly Report form is in itself fully explanatory
except insomuch as an intelligent assessment of the
percentage of full completion of each block, in the case
of the Housing Branch, is required.
The need for these percentage figures to have an
appropriate accuracy is that when progress on site is
being monitored by the officers of the Sites Managers
Group at County Hall 'equivalents' in partially completed
buildings are counted in as well as completed buildings
in assessment of the overall progress of the contract.
Therefore some accuracy in assessment of the percentage
of full completion of each housing block is necessary.

21 Safety

It is the responsibility of the main contractor to ensure
that he complies with the requirements of the Health and
Safety at Work Act, and the Factories Act as set out in
the Construction Regulations. Should the Clerk of
Works, in his opinion, consider this is not the case,
particularly in regard to access to various parts of the
building, he should report to the Department by
telephone and make a note in his diary.
The contractor is required by his contract to provide
safety helmets for the use of the Clerk of Works and
Council Officers visiting the site. It is recommended that
such protective clothing should be worn at all times when
carrying out inspections on the site.

22 Labour disputes

Immediately the Clerk of Works is aware of a labour
dispute on or affecting his site, of whatsoever degree,
official or unofficial, he is to:
1 Inform the architect-in-charge by telephone
2 Inform Sites Manager by telephone, in the case
   of the Housing Branch
3 Confirm by short written report to the architect-in-
   charge the same evening, with a copy to the Labour
   Relations Officer.

4 Note the circumstances in his diary and in Weekly
 Report.
The Building & Civil Engineering Industries have their
own working rule agreements which provides conciliation
machinery for dealing with disputes. The decision to
implement it is left to the two parties in the dispute.
The Clerk of Works is not to involve himself in any way,
either by comment, advice or any other action, in any
labour dispute, negotiation, or discussion between a
contractor and his labour force. He must hold himself
strictly and impartially aloof from these proceedings,
confining his attention to reporting as instructed.

2 Commencement of a Contract

1 Briefing meetings

Before each contract is commenced a detailed briefing meeting is held in County Hall at which the contractor meets the architect-in-charge and attendant officers. The contract is discussed, and contract documents and drawings are handed to the contractor.
Before the briefing meeting the Clerk of Works should obtain a small-scale layout of the site, and should visit the site, so that he is familiar with the site location, configuration, boundaries, spoil clearance position, adjoining owners, etc. The Clerk of Works will then attend the briefing meeting, upon notification by the Sites Manager in the case of the Housing Branch, and will normally be issued with his contract documents, including drawings, at that time.

2 Handing-over of site

Normally arrangements will be made for the Clerk of Works to be present at the handing-over of the site to the contractor, and he should commence his site diary and register of drawings from that day. The Clerk of Works will receive a copy of the Order to Commence and should make note of the contract times allowed for the various portions of the work.

3 Siting of offices

The Clerk of Works is to see that the contractor obtains the approval of the architect-in-charge to the siting of temporary offices and stores: and it will be normal for this to be settled at the meeting for the handing over of the site. The Clerk of Works' office should be sited in a suitably strategic position so that the main part of the work is in view. The size of the office and the equipment to be provided are specified and the Clerk of Works should see that they are in accordance with the specification. In the case of the Housing Branch the Clerk of Works should obtain the agreement of the Sites Manager to the siting, size, and equipment of the Clerk of Works' personal office, and the conference room.

4 Telephone

Unless otherwise particularly specified a separate telephone line is required for the Clerk of Works and is required right to the end of the contract, and he is to see that the contractor makes application to the GPO for the telephone line as early in the contract as possible. As soon as his telephone is installed the Clerk of Works should inform the Department. The Council checks and pays the charges made for calls from the Clerk of Works telephone.

5 Datum points for setting out and levelling

The Clerk of Works is to see that the correct Bench Marks, referred to in the specification, are known to the contractor, and that the contractor is perfectly clear as to the building line, setting out points, and site boundaries.

9

| 6 | **Trees** | The Clerk of Works is to ensure that the terms of the specification with regard to retention and protection of trees on site are followed, and should make early arrangements under instruction from the architect-in-charge that the trees for retention are clearly marked. |

| 7 | **Contractor's name boards** | If the contractor, as is usual, wishes to erect a main board giving his name and address and possibly those of his sub-contractors, the position of the board is to be approved by the architect-in-charge, and the board is to be headed 'GREATER LONDON COUNCIL CONTRACT' in an approved style of lettering. The Clerk of Works should note that no other advertisements nor any individual sub-contractors' boards are to be permitted on the site. The contractor may wish to erect further boards giving the contractor's name and address. This may be done provided they are headed 'GREATER LONDON COUNCIL CONTRACT'. For the ILEA all boards are to be headed 'INNER LONDON EDUCATION AUTHORITY'. |

| 8 | **Council notice boards** | Under instruction from the architect-in-charge the Clerk of Works is to make early arrangements for the erection of the Greater London Council notice board giving, in the case of the Housing Branch, the title of the estate and the number of dwellings, and showing the Council crest. The Housing Branch notice boards are detailed on Departmental Standard Drawing Nos. D.3120, D.3124, D.3121 and D.3125. |

| 9 | **Bulk supplies** | The Clerk of Works is to see that at the commencement of the contract the contractor has all the necessary requisition forms for bulk supply articles, that he understands them fully, and that he sends the completed forms in at an early date in accordance with the instructions given in the specification. Copies of these requisitions should be retained by the Clerk of Works. |

| 10 | **Existing services** | The Clerk of Works is to make himself immediately conversant by means of the contract drawings and documents, and, if necessary, through contact with the Local Authority, of the positions of all existing services, water, gas, electricity, and sewage, on or under the site, noting particularly those services in the area of the excavation. He should then see that the contractor deals with these services in the manner specified, instruction being sought as necessary from the architect-in-charge. |

| 11 | **Levels over site** | It will be necessary for the Clerk of Works, at the commencement of the contract, to recheck and record the site levels in the form of a level grid. Instructions |

for this are given under 'SITE LEVELS AND BOUNDARIES'.

12 Pavements

At the commencement of a contract the Clerk of Works is to make a check of pavements immediately adjoining the site with the contractor and agree with a representative of the Local Authority concerned the existing state of damage to paving slabs. This will obviate any misunderstanding that might occur at the end of the contract as to the responsibility for breakages.

3 Site Levels and Boundaries

1   Surface levels of site

It is essential that before any surface excavation or any other reduction or making up of levels is carried out on the site an accurate level grid of the site is recorded. It is sometimes the case that because parts of the site were covered with buildings demolished only at a very late stage, a sufficiently comprehensive series of levels could not be obtained prior to the commencement of the building contract.

For this reason amongst others, it is necessary that a check level grid of the site be carried out immediately following the issue of the Order to Commence.

This will usually be mentioned to both the contractor and the Clerk of Works at the briefing meeting, and the contractor will be asked to carry out the work under the supervision and check of the Clerk of Works. The Clerk of Works. however. may well have to take the initiative to ensure that the work is carried out, and at an early date.

2   Fly tipping

It is sometimes found that unauthorised fly-tipping has occurred on a site. It is usual for arrangements to be made with the Valuer, to remove the fly-tipped material as a first operation, under separate accounting arrangements, and the Clerk of Works should make an accurate count of the amount removed. Thereafter the site grid should represent the site configuration without the fly-tipped material.

If vehicles are discovered fly-tipping on a Greater London Council site no attempt should be made by the Clerk of Works actively to interfere. If the site has not yet been handed over to the contractor, however, the Clerk of Works should report the circumstances of the fly-tipping to the architect-in-charge who will transmit that information to the Valuer.

If the contractor has possession of the site the matter will be the contractor's responsibility and he will be expected to deal with it.

3   Agreement and recording of surface levels

The levels, as they are taken, should be agreed between the Clerk of Works and the Site Agent or the representative of the contractor, and they should be recorded on a plan of the site. The level record plan should be signed by the Clerk of Works and the Site Agent. Four prints at least should be taken, two copies are to be forwarded to the architect-in-charge for the record, one copy retained by the Clerk of Works and one copy handed to the contractor's Site Agent for his retention.

The Clerk of Works should see that no reduction or other alteration of levels takes place until the architect-in-charge has seen the check levels and has issued instructions that such work may proceed. If during the taking of the check levels significant differences from the expected levels are apparent then the architect-in-charge should be informed immediately so that amongst other considerations he may arrange for the Valuer to be called in to see the differences that have been noted.

4	**Level book**	The Clerk of Works' level book must be properly written up in accordance with the levelling method adopted and must show the readings from which the levels were calculated.
5	**Datum for levels**	Levels are in every case to be related to the datum level specified in the contract documents.
6	**Adjoining property**	It is a Clerk of Works responsibility that during construction the department are good neighbours as far as adjoining owners are concerned. Arrangements (including fencing arrangements) which have been agreed with adjoining owners, and which are specified in contract documents, must not be varied in any particular without referring such proposed variation to the architect-in-charge for instructions. This is to ensure that no legal contractual arrangements made by the Council with parties having interests in adjoining properties are upset or prejudiced by action of the contractor or his representatives. Directly it becomes known to a Clerk of Works that a contractor contemplates any variation from the instructions issued to him upon such matters, he is immediately to enter a protest and report the circumstances forthwith to the architect-in-charge.
7	**Damage to property**	In the event of any damage to property the Clerk of Works is to make immediate report to the architect-in-charge when he will be instructed whether certified statements and witnesses' names will be required. The Clerk of Works should also make note of the incident in his diary.
8	**Adjoining contracts**	Clerks of Works are to ensure that contractors do not encroach upon areas allocated to other contractors, either in the execution of work, or in the storage of materials.
9	**Completed services**	Prior to the practical completion of the contract for each portion of the work the Clerk of Works is to have marked on a plan the details of the drainage, gas, water, telephone and electricity services as executed. He is to forward the marked up plan to the architect-in-charge at the completion of the work. These details will normally

have been noted on the working drawings by the Clerk of Works when the services were being put in.

10 Site boundaries

Before the contractor proceeds with work on party walls or fences the Clerk of Works should inform the architect-in-charge that such work is due to be commenced.
It will normally be necessary for the boundaries of sites with adjacent properties to be specifically defined and set out by the Council's surveyors, and this will be arranged by the architect-in-charge.

11 Street lighting

In cases where lamp standards for electrical street lighting are installed by sub-contract to the main contract, it will be the duty of the Clerk of Works to check the setting out of the standards; and for this work the exact positions of the LEB branch lighting cables across roads and pavements must be known and recorded. Where the roads have been constructed under separate contract the Clerk of Works (Housing Branch) must obtain, from his opposite number in the Housing Engineer's Division, and record on his drawings, the exact position of these cables and cable junctions.

12 Temporary fencing owned by the Council

Where a contractor puts up fencing around a site there is usually some Council fencing to be dismantled and placed for collection; on some occasions the Council fencing remains to the end of the contract when the contractor is to take it down and place it ready for collection.
In either case it is the Clerk of Works' responsibility that no fencing belonging to the Council is lost. Clerks of Works therefore, at the handing over of a site to the contractor, are to check the amount of Council fencing in the contract and to note this on the Weekly Report and in the Diary. In the case of Housing Sites, when the fencing is dismantled, the Clerk of Works should inform the local officer of the Director of Housing by memorandum that the fencing is available for his collection. A note should then be made in the Weekly Report and the Clerk of Works' diary that this has been done.

4 Contract Documents

1 Form of contract

The Department uses the 'RIBA Local Authority Conditions of Contract' modified for use by the Greater London Council and the Inner London Education Authority, shown therein as the case may be, as the 'Employer'. In all major jobs, the Department uses 'Contract Bills' which include the preliminaries and are in effect a combined specification and bill separated out into trades.

The material and workmanship clauses for each trade, printed with the bill of quantities for each trade, are termed Work Section Preambles, or Trade Preambles. In smaller contracts a specification, also containing preliminary clauses, is bound in one volume with the conditions of contract and there are no Bills of Quantities. Under the form of contract, the tender, the Articles of Agreement and the Conditions of Contract are accompanied by:

> Contract Drawings
> Contract Bills (which include Preliminaries and material and workmanship preambles for each trade) or specification; and these alone are the contract documents.

2 Contract drawings

The Contract Drawings comprise
> Set A—drawings which accompany the tender
> and
> Set B—drawings issued with the Order to Commence.
Included with Set B are drawings showing schedules of work relating to:

> Sub-structure and concrete
> Brickwork and fixing joinery
> Direct Supply items and plumbing
> Ironmongery
> Finishings
> Painting and Decorating
> Drainage
> Paving and Earthworks

3 Clerk of Works in the form of contract

Under the form of contract the Clerk of Works' duty is to act solely as inspector on behalf of the Employer under the direction of the architect.

It is important to note that the Clerk of Works may give directions to the contractor or his 'foreman upon the works' *but* that these directions will have no effect

1 unless they are in regard to a matter upon which the architect is empowered by the Conditions to issue instructions (see below); and
2 unless confirmed in writing by the architect within two working days.

4 Matters on which the architect is empowered to issue instructions

In general the architect is empowered by the Conditions to issue instructions on the following matters:
1 Variations to the work, including variations to comply with statutory obligations.
2 Expenditure of provisional and p.c. sums.
3 Discrepancies between the contract documents.
4 Appointment of nominated sub-contractors, and nominated suppliers.
5 Postponement of any portion of the work.
6 Opening up work for inspection, or testing work, materials or goods.
7 Removal of faulty work, materials or goods.
8 Dismissal of any person.
9 Rectification of defects.
10 Action in case of war.
11 Errors in setting out.
12 Disposal of antiquities.

5 Confirmations within two working days

As discussed in the section dealing with the 'Duties and responsibilities of a Clerk of Works', with regard to the confirmation within two working days of the Clerk of Works' directions, it is considered that contractors will not in this respect observe the letter of the contract for the majority of the directions given by the Clerk of Works. Nevertheless the Clerk of Works should arrange a procedure in advance with his architect-in-charge, so that if a Site Instruction that may be arguable is resisted by the contractor, a confirmation can be in the contractor's office within two working days.
As indicated it may not often be necessary to use this procedure but when it is required it needs to be readily available.

6 Timely supply of information

There are certain specified causes of delay and disturbance for which an extension of time will be granted and for which a claim has to be entertained. One of these is the non-receipt by the contractor from the architect in due time of information in the form of necessary instructions, drawings, details or levels, for which the contractor has applied at an appropriate time. It is therefore necessary that a Clerk of Works should endeavour to foresee, well in advance, any need for instructions, drawings, details or levels, so that he may advise the architect-in-charge accordingly.
Whilst it should be noted that the contractor is specifically required to apply in writing for the information he requires, and has the responsibility of making this written request at a time which is reasonable in comparison to the contract completion date, the architect is still responsible for supplying information at the right time. The Clerk of Works therefore should on no account delay

his notification to the architect-in-charge that information will be required.

7 Extension of time of completion

The following are the causes of delay for which an extension of contract time is to be granted:
1 Late information, in the form of necessary instructions, drawings, details or levels.
2 Delay by nominated sub-contractors or by nominated suppliers.
3 Delay by direct contractors or artists.
4 Variations, discrepancies in contract documents, or postponement of work.
5 Strikes, civil troubles, fire, force majeure, or exceptionally inclement weather.
6 Opening up or testing work, materials or goods, which are found to be satisfactory.
7 Unforeseen difficulty to secure labour and materials.

8 Stoppages

It is worthy of particular note that it is the responsibility of all Clerks of Works in the Department to record day by day in the Weekly Report the precise number of men who are stopped through any cause (including inclement weather), the precise number of hours, or days, the stoppage covers, and if it is due to inclement weather, a description with some evaluation of the weather concerned. Where tower cranes or other tall plant are on site, a note of high winds causing a stop of crane working should be made.

9 Nominated sub-contractors and suppliers

Under the contract
1 The contractor may not grant an extension of time to a nominated sub-contractor without the written consent of the architect, i.e., the architect is a party to the agreement that the extension is justified. This consent to the extension would normally only be given where the delay in the sub-contract was not due to the sub-contractor's own faults.
2 An extension of time is to be granted to the main contractor if there is delay on the part of the nominated sub-contractor, provided that the extension is only for the period by which the main contract was in fact delayed, and that the main contractor had taken all reasonable steps to reduce such delay.
3 If the nominated sub-contractor fails to complete the sub-contract works in the time specified in the sub-contract plus extensions, and the architect is of the opinion that he should reasonably have done so, the architect will certify accordingly in writing. It is the Clerk of Works' duty to ensure that every bit of information on the progress of the sub-contract is ready and available to the architect when required.

The certification the architect has to make is quite a serious matter for the sub-contractor, as it may be used by the main contractor to obtain damages from the sub-contractor.

4 In the case of nominated suppliers delaying the contract by late supply the main contractor may claim an extension of time.

For these various reasons the Clerk of Works should pay particular attention to the deliveries, the work and the progress of the nominated sub-contractors, and the adequacy, the timeliness, and the quality of nominated suppliers' deliveries.

10 Care of drawings

A proper register of drawings, with dates of receipt, is to be compiled and kept up to date by the Clerk of Works. Drawings are to be kept in a neat orderly fashion ready of access when required.

11 Amendments to drawings and documents

When instructions are issued by the architect-in-charge, or decisions are taken on site, amending dimensions or detail, the drawing concerned is to be marked up immediately in ball-point pen or crayon by the Clerk of Works, showing the new dimension or detail; the various services should be indicated by distinctive and different colours; or if a variation drawing has been issued the original drawing is to be endorsed in ball-point pen or crayon accordingly. The Clerk of Works is to make any necessary amendments to the Specification or Contract Bills in a similar manner.

12 Index to Specification or Contract Bills

The Clerk of Works will find it most useful to add to any index of the Specification or Contract Bills by tagging the clauses he specially needs to note.

13 Return of documents

The Clerk of Works is to return to the architect-in-charge on the completion of the contract, all drawings, specification, bill of quantities, copies of orders, and site diary. The properly marked up copy of the contractor's programme showing the stage by stage progress of the contract from inception to completion is to be sent by the Clerk of Works to the Sites Manager, in the case of the Housing Branch, or to the Superintendent of Works in the case of the Schools Division.

14 Completion certificates

The copies of official orders for the execution of works or the supply of goods constitute, when signed and certified by the Clerk of Works, ' Satisfactory Completion Certificates ', and they are to be forwarded to the department promptly upon satisfactory completion of the work.

5 Progress of Works

1 Responsibility of Clerk of Works for progress

As in the case of all other staff connected with the contract the Clerk of Works bears a certain element of responsibility for the satisfactory progress of the contract and its final completion to contract time. The Clerk of Works must keep in mind the contract completion date from the beginning of the contract; he must ensure that no action, or lack of action, on his part, causes avoidable delay in the carrying out of the work, and he must maintain pressure on the contractor so that the completion dates that the contract demands, or in special cases that Divisional policy requires, are in fact achieved.

The really expert Clerk of Works can exert a most valuable influence on the progress of a contract and the completion of individual blocks within the time required.

It is incumbent upon all Clerks of Works in all divisions of the Housing Branch, who may be in charge of contracts that:

1 They are to be in possession of an approved programme of works (with adequate space for marking up) and they are to keep this marked with the up-to-date progress position of each individual block.

2 They are to ensure that a revised up-to-date programme is provided by the contractor if the original programme gets too far out of date.

3 Special measures are sometimes necessary to achieve annual programmes of completions and, in conjunction with the architect-in-charge, and the Sites Manager, the Clerk of Works will be expected to participate fully in the measures necessary to achieve these programmes.

4 At the completion of the Housing Branch contract and before re-posting the Clerk of Works is to deliver the marked up copy of the programme (original and if necessary, revised copies) to the Sites Manager who will discuss any particularly outstanding aspects of the contract's overall progress.

2 Weekly report—to chart progress of the works and factors that affect that progress

The primary purpose of the Weekly Report made by the Clerk of Works is to record and keep check of the progress of the work.

Two copies should be sent to the Department, and one copy be retained by the Clerk of Works.

It should be noted that the position on the progress of the work should be stated with sufficient precision for the officer who reads the report fully to appreciate the situation without having to refer to previous reports. The actual progress position should be related to the current programme and should be given in weeks. In the case of the Housing Branch, trades progress should be shown in the body of the report by trade percentage figures for each floor of each block. The Clerk of Works is to indicate, in the 'Progress Report' columns of his Weekly Report, the precise date of the physical start of each individual block, the 'physical start' being the first concrete laid, as part of the foundations.

The column ' Drawings and information required ' should be completed after consultation with the contractor's Site Agent.

3 Records of labour

An accurate return is to be made of the labour employed on the site each day, recording separately the craftsmen, labourers and apprentices. In the case of sub-contract labour the name of the firm, and trade, should be stated. Overtime hours and the absence of a necessary Overtime Permit should also be noted.

4 Record of stoppages

It is most important that all Clerks of Works in the department record day by day in the Weekly Report the precise number of men who are stopped, through any cause whatsoever (including inclement weather), the precise number of hours, or days, the stoppage covers, and if it is due to inclement weather, a description with some evaluation of the weather concerned.

5 Potential causes of delay

General observations by the Clerk of Works, in the Weekly Report, on site progress or other relevant matters are of considerable value in assessing the position on the site and some general observations should invariably be made by the Clerk of Works. The Clerk of Works must specifically note any items that are delaying, or in the future may delay, the execution of the work.

Potential causes of delay which should be noted may be insufficient or inadequacy of labour or plant; delays in material deliveries; lack of timely information on drawings; ineffective co-ordination of sub-contractors and delay in a sub-contractor commencing work; or any lack on the contractor's part in organising, or arranging a proper sequence of the work.

6 Progress charts

The contractor will be required to produce within one month of the Order to Commence a programme of works which should be an effective instrument for the contractor's site progress control, and which should be reviewed and revised as necessary during the course of the work. The Clerk of Works is to use a copy of this programme as a Progress Chart, and record weekly the progress position of the works; the completely marked up programme should be returned to the Department at the end of the contract. The contractor's programme of work should include all major finishing trades and should be the basis for compiling periodical progress returns for Site Meetings. An up to date programme is of course necessary for this, and it follows that if a contractor's programme gets seriously out of date a revised programme should be requested. This matter can appropriately be brought up at a Site Meeting.

7 Site meetings

Progress is one of the primary matters for consideration at the Site Meetings held by the architect-in-charge, and the Clerk of Works is to see that he is fully apprised of all items adversely affecting progress, so that these matters may be fully examined at the meeting.

At each Site Meeting the Clerk of Works should have ready in duplicate for the architect-in-charge, a statement of the progress position on each building and the number of weeks each building is ahead of or behind the current programme.

8 Marking up progress charts

The Clerk of Works is to keep his Progress Chart up to date at least weekly, and the three line method of marking-up is to be used.

The top line should show the actual percentage of work done, in red (compared to the contractor's programme); the second line is the contractor's programme for the operation, in black; and the third line the actual time taken, in green.

The marked up Progress Chart is to be exhibited on the wall of the Clerk of Works' office. This chart at the end of the contract is one of the documents that has to be preserved.

9 Routine records of progress matters

With labour-only sub-contracting gangs for main trades, the question of progressing contracts, and how the Clerk of Works should play an active part in this, requires consideration.

Firstly, as has been stated, the Clerk of Works is to continuously record progress, clearly, against the contractor's programme and progress chart and have this on exhibit in his office.

Secondly, the Clerk of Works is to keep the architect-in-charge fully apprised, weekly, of any fall-off in progress in any particular trade, and give the architect-in-charge an opinion as to the reasons for this fall-off.

Thirdly, the Clerk of Works is to provide the architect-in-charge with a clear statement at each site meeting of the progress position of every part of the contract, agreed in advance with the contractor's agent, so that the matter may be taken up at that meeting, and the contractor will be asked to give his own reasons, for the record, for any delays that have occurred.

10 Progress difficulties

There has been deterioration of late years in the general efficiency of the building industry, and its capacity to appropriately progress work of adequate quality. This is due largely to the serious shortages of skilled and experienced trades supervisory personnel in the industry, and the growing dependence upon labour-only subcontracting gangs, paid sometimes at high rates, but often without adequate skills, and without the necessary trades foremen to properly supervise their work.

This often involves the Clerk of Works in considerable time wastage in checking, repeatedly guiding, teaching, and almost directly supervising trade gangs. This is not good enough and takes up too much of the Clerk of Works' time that should be spent on his other duties. Where there is insufficient trade supervision on any job the Clerk of Works should consult with the architect-in-charge and the position should be ventilated at an early site meeting, the contractor being strongly requested to provide the necessary trades foremen for the proper supervision of the work.

11 Errors involving loss of time

The Clerk of Works is to note in his Job Diary where, and when, work has had to be pulled down, cut away rebuilt, or replaced, involving loss of time, the amount of time lost, and a note as to how the sequence of the later work was affected.

6 Instructions to Contractors

1 Additional works

No orders whatever, either written or verbal, may be given by the Clerk of Works involving work or cost additional to that provided in the contract, without prior instruction from the architect-in-charge. Should the necessity for additional work arise, the question is to be referred immediately to the architect-in-charge and no additional work is to be put in hand until the official instruction is given.

2 Site instructions by Clerk of Works

Should it become essential in exceptional circumstances for the Clerk of Works to give immediate written site instructions, permission is to be obtained from the architect-in-charge, by telephone if necessary.

1 To ensure that the instructions which may have to be given to contractors are issued in a standard form, and that copies are appropriately circulated, books of instruction forms in sets are provided and must be used for giving out all site instructions.

2 The forms will be completed and issued by Clerks of Works:

(a) To convey instructions to the contractor by the Clerks of Works on behalf of the architect.

(b) To confirm oral instructions given by the Clerk of Works on behalf of the architect.

(c) To convey or confirm instructions given by the architect on the site.

Written confirmation of oral instructions must be given on the same day.

3 The top copy of the instruction form will be delivered by the Clerk of Works to the contractor's representative on the site and the other copies distributed as follows:

1 copy—to be retained by the Clerk of Works in the book;

2 copies—to be sent by the Clerk of Works each week with the weekly report to the architect (one of which would be forwarded by the architect at his discretion to the Principal Quantity Surveyor or appointed managing quantity surveyor).

4 It will also be necessary to issue site instructions in the matter of heating and electrical works to the contractor for his heating and electrical sub-contractors. These instructions will normally originate with the heating or electrical inspectors. These may be given orally subject to a written record being issued through the building contractor the same day. Books similar to those mentioned above will be issued to Inspectors, but an extra copy will be available for the sub-contractor. The Inspector will prepare his instruction and both he and the Clerk of Works will sign it.

5 When issuing site instructions, whether they will involve a formal variation order or not, consideration must be given to any possible effect on other trades. Thus, the Clerk of Works or Inspector, must inform each other of site instructions which may affect the building work or engineering services. It will help in this if site instructions are passed quickly to the persons concerned so that they may make a rapid assessment of the effect on their own work.

6 Instruction forms are to be numbered serially throughout the contract by the Clerk of Works.

3 Dayworks

When daywork has been authorised, the Clerk of Works is to check the work done, the material used and the man hours and machine hours expended. He should sign and date each daywork sheet, endorsing it as follows:

' Subject to approval by the architect as daywork I certify that the time and materials as stated are correct.'

A record must be made on the Weekly Report, and in the Clerk of Works' diary, of all daywork sheets signed. In the event of disagreement with the items recorded on daywork sheets, such matters should be referred to architect-in-charge for decision.

4 Contractor's vouchers

It is the practice of some contractors to present their inter-office vouchers (as distinct from authorised daywork vouchers) to a Clerk of Works for his signature, notifying items regarded by the contractor as qualifying under the the heading of extra or additional works.

These vouchers are NOT to be signed by the Clerk of Works. Even though these vouchers may be annotated by the contractor as ' for record purposes only ' they should not be signed by the Clerk of Works.

Where a contractor presses the acceptance of these vouchers on the grounds that under the relevant clause of the contract they form the contractor's notification of works deemed additional to that shown on original contract documents, then the Clerk of Works should arrange that the vouchers are forwarded to the architect-in-charge who will deal with the matter.

5 Contractor's paysheets

It is also the practice of some contractors to present copies of their paysheets to the Clerk of Works for signature. These paysheets give names, trades' hours worked, rates and total pay of the labour employed. As the Clerk of Works is not in a position to check any of these items no useful purpose is served by appending a signature, and these paysheets should not therefore be signed by a Clerk of Works.

6   Instruction to correct defective work

In the normal course of the contract there sometimes occurs faulty work which, in the view of the Clerk of Works, should be pulled down or taken out. This is sometimes so obvious that the contractor, realising his mistake as soon as his attention is drawn to it, at once prepares to remedy the fault; and in such cases unless structural or aesthetic considerations are involved, a simple notification to the architect-in-charge and a record in the weekly report and diary will suffice. In all other cases however it will be necessary to issue a formal site instruction.

Where such formal instruction is issued to the contractor to remove or remedy defective work for which the contractor is responsible then it must be made completely clear that it relates to defective work which is the contractor's responsibility.

In every instance where an instruction is required the architect-in-charge should be informed in detail of the circumstance; and the method of instruction, and the time of confirmation of the instruction, agreed with him. If there occurs poor work, not necessarily the subject of a 'pulling down' instruction, which the contractor obstinately or evasively fails to remedy (or if the contractor persistently fails to comply, although warned, with any of the contract particulars), then the Clerk of Works is to advise the architect-in-charge of the circumstance in writing so that appropriate action may be taken. In the Housing Branch a copy of this advice is to be sent to the Sites Manager.

7 Site Investigations

1 General

In general a Site Clerk of Works is not directly involved in site investigation, which is completed in practically every case before the commencement of the contract. Clerks of Works however are sometimes seconded to the Sites Managers group for specialist duties in connection with site investigations; and there are some occasions in the excavation of the very mixed soils under London when some unexpected features are revealed, possibly necessitating, often at the District Surveyor's request, the carrying out of plate loading tests on site.

The contract drawings include trial bore layouts and strata section sheets in the site set of drawings on all contracts. Therefore, as a Clerk of Works may at some stage be required to participate in some phase of site investigation a few general notes on the subject would be appropriate.

2 First investigation of a site

The first examination, or reconnaissance, of a site is carried out before the site is purchased by the Council. In Housing Branch the Site Planning Research group examine the site for overall suitability, and as part of this a reconnaissance is carried out by the Sites Manager's group with specific reference to the type of subsoil, any particular foundation difficulties that may be met, and the likely relative cost of foundation works, and of abnormals.

This involves gathering information locally and from all sources; geological survey and museum; local borough; previous user; District Surveyor; building inspector; gravel pit records; examination of neighbouring sites and works; and where necessary includes shallow hand bores using a Mackintosh prospecting tool.

A Ground Condition report is formulated by the Sites Manager's group, for the SPR group's information when the latter are making their recommendations to the Valuer.

3 Soils investigation by specialist firms

The next step after the site has been allocated to the Branch is for a scientific soils engineering investigation to be carried out under contract by a specialist firm. The Sites Manager's group, in close liaison with the Structural Engineer operate term contracts, re-tendered at three year intervals, for the soils investigation by specialist firms, covering London in four areas.

These highly specialised firms carry out trial borings, obtain samples of soils from varying appropriate depths, take necessary site tests, eg, penetrations, carry out full analyses and laboratory tests of the samples taken, and produce a report with observations and recommendations.

4 Primary purpose of term contracts

The primary purpose of the term contract is
1 To assess and make recommendations for bearing capacities;
2 To assess settlements;
for the information of the Structural Engineer in his design of the foundations of the project.

5 Other soils engineering problems

The specialist firms concerned are equipped to investigate and produce recommendations for the solution of many other soils engineering problems; and recommendations are often sought on such problems, eg. slip, clay surface creep, compaction of spoil, soakaway permeabilities and water movements, on behalf of and in liaison with the Structural Engineer, or other divisions, branches or departments.

6 Chemical analyses

Sulphate analyses from water and soil samples are carried out under separate arrangements.

7 Co-ordination of theory and practice

It can be said that with the preliminary investigations of neighbourhood works, the scientific soil mechanics investigations by specialist laboratories, and the participation of the Structural Engineer and the District Surveyor with the information available to them, and their actual down to earth practical examination of the excavations for foundations on the site, that the best possible co-ordination of scientific soil mechanics theory with hard experience and the best engineering practice is almost certainly realised.

8 Spacing of trial bores

Spacing of 15 m. in both directions is appropriate for a building site. When it is considered that boreholes within metres of each other in the London area can reveal very differing conditions this coverage of 230 square metres of ground by only one 150 mm. diameter borehole is seen to be by no means too much. It is a matter of some interest when considering how much ground we are actually sampling in proportion to the whole site, that a 90 m. grid, sometimes used for preliminary explorations, means only one 150 mm. diameter borehole per approximately 0.8 hectares of ground.
It is also to be noted that all specialist firms, carrying out term contracts ' for site investigations, issue disclaimers of responsibility for conditions between borehole positions '.

9 Sub-soil soundings

The use of intermediate sub-soil soundings or other type of penetration field tests, in areas between bores, although not particularly favoured by specialist firms can often reveal in a direct and relatively inexpensive manner hazards to economic foundation construction.

10 Code of Practice   The relevant Code of Practice, Site Investigations is C.P. 2001 (1957).

8 Foundations

1 Setting out foundations

The Clerk of Works is to check in detail that the contractor's setting out corresponds exactly to drawings. The Clerk of Works should also see that main centre lines are beaconed in concrete, or in timber set in concrete, clear of excavation and reasonably free from possibility of disturbance so that the setting out may be rechecked at any later stage of the foundation work.

A steel tape should be used for checking dimensions. In the event of any variation of setting out becoming necessary, instructions must be obtained from the architect-in-charge, and the variation recorded in red ink on the setting out plan.

2 Bottoms of excavations

The bottom of every excavation for foundations will normally be inspected and passed by the architect-in-charge, the structural engineer, and the District Surveyor or Local Authority's representative before any concrete is placed. The passing of foundations does not devolve upon the Clerk of Works.

When depths have been reached at which inspection is desirable, and the excavated widths and lines have been checked, the Clerk of Works is to inform the architect-in-charge who will arrange for the necessary inspection.

The Clerk of Works is to take and record the levels of the approved bottoms before concrete is placed. When foundations bottoms are approved concreting should take place without delay.

3 Excavation beyond contract depth

It is essential that the architect-in-charge gives prior approval to any work which may involve the Council in cost additional to the contract amount. In particular is this so with foundations, and the Clerk of Works must therefore obtain prior approval from the architect-in-charge before permitting the contractor to excavate below the contract depth. While in most cases the request for approval will be formality only, this formal procedure is to be followed through in every case of excavation beyond contract depth.

For these reasons the Clerk of Works is to:

1 Make himself aware of the contract depth of all foundations.

2 As excavation proceeds check whether it is possible to obtain a satisfactory foundation at depths shallower than contract depth, and if so, inform the architect-in-charge and request Structural Engineer's inspection at that depth.

3 Stop excavation within a few inches of contract depth for Structural Engineer's examination and instruction.

29

4 Report in every case, for confirmatory approval before work proceeds, to architect-in-charge, whenever instruction is issued by Senior Structural Engineer or District Surveyor to go deeper than contract depth, or to widen or otherwise increase a foundation.

If a Clerk of Works has any difficulty in implementing this instruction with a contractor the Sites Manager is to be informed.

4 Visits of Structural Engineers to Sites

Whenever a visiting Structural Engineer has occasion to instruct any modification or variation of any sort on site, the Clerk of Works, will report the instruction (immediately and before any work proceeds in the special case of foundations) to the architect-in-charge and send a copy to him by post the same day.

5 Concreting foundations

The Clerk of Works is to satisfy himself, before concrete is placed, that the foundation bottoms are clean and trimmed and that the materials, the mix, the water content and the methods of mixing, transporting and placing the concrete are completely adequate and fully in conformity with the specification.

When concreting of foundations is in progress the Clerk of Works is to give continuous supervision and on no account may he leave the works except by specific prior permission of the architect-in-charge and except also when the necessary relief Clerk of Works has taken over. On completion of a foundation the Clerk of Works is to check and record the finished concrete levels before brickwork is commenced and is to note the check in his Weekly Report and in his diary.

6 Records of foundations

The Clerk of Works is to make precise day to day detailed records of foundation work as the work proceeds. Immediately upon completion of the foundations of any one block, or other structure, the Clerk of Works is to prepare a tracing on cloth or paper, in black Indian ink, giving complete details in plan form of the foundation work to that building. The drawing is to include:

1 Contract title, block identification and all necessary overall dimensions.
2 The datum level and GF finished level.
3 The depths of all trenches, with all changes of level and all relative ground levels.
4 The width of all trenches, with lengths and widths of breaks.
5 The dimensions of piers.
6 The top levels of concrete in the foundations.
7 The date the various sections of concrete were poured.

8 The mixes of concrete used and the use of any
special cement.
9 Space for signature by contractor's agent, Clerk of
Works and architect-in-charge.
The drawings are to be agreed with the contractor
as being a true record of the work and are to be signed
by the Contractor's Site Agent, by the Clerk of Works
and by the architect-in-charge. Dyeline prints are then
to be taken and distributed as follows :—
1 copy — Contractor
1 copy — Council QS
1 copy — SE (or Consultant)
1 copy — Clerk of Works
1 copy — Sites Manager (in the case of the Housing
Branch)
Original — Section Architect
In the Housing Branch, the ordering of dyeline prints
may be arranged via the Sites Manager's office. In
addition to the foundation record drawings, Clerks of
Works, of all divisions, are asked to forward to the
Sites Manager a summary of foundation details, block
by block, for all structures on their contract. These are
for record in connection with site investigations and
Ground Condition reports. The details should be filled
in on a form H.O. 251 obtainable from the Sites Manager's
office and of which a copy is shown, attached in this
Section.

7	**Physical start to individual blocks**	The Clerk of Works is to indicate, in the ' Progress Report ' columns of his Weekly Report, the precise date of the physical start of each individual block the ' physical start ' being the first concrete laid, as part of the foundations.
8	**Records of obstructions**	Where there are obstructions in excavation such as old concrete work, old brickwork or old services sufficiently massive and durable to impede appreciably the operation by the excavation method that is being adopted, then a record of obstructions precisely dimensioned and detailed is to be prepared by the Clerk of Works, similar to but separate from the record of foundations.
9	**Piled foundations**	In the case of piled foundations the Clerk of Works is to keep a record of the progress of the piling on a copy of the pile layout plan. This plan should be kept up to date daily, showing the piles driven each day, the dates of driving, the set obtained and the results of tests made, if any. In addition the Clerk of Works is to complete a Daily Pile Driving Record, on a pro forma supplied by the Department, in triplicate. One copy is to be retained on

site and two copies forwarded to the architect-in-charge with the Weekly Report.

10 Water in excavated foundations

Where running water or a 'spring' is encountered in foundations the Clerk of Works is to inform the architect-in-charge so that instructions may be issued for dealing with the matter adequately. Where continuous pumping is found to be necessary and there is a possible danger of drawing water from near foundations the Clerk of Works is immediately to inform the architect-in-charge who will issue instructions.

11 Extent of excavations

The Clerk of Works is to ensure that excavation for a foundation does not in any way endanger adjacent foundations or piling, by being excessively sloped back, improperly strutted or extended to an undue distance outside its own boundaries. In bad ground there is often the possibility of this occurring.
If in the Clerk of Works' opinion there is any likelihood of adjacent foundations being at all affected, then the Clerk of Works should halt the work of excavation and seek instructions immediately from the architect-in-charge.

12 Safety in excavations

It is a requirement of the Council's specification that the contractor maintain excavations in a safe and satisfactory manner. If at any time, in the opinion of the Clerk of of Works, excavations are not being maintained in such manner, e.g., excavation to depth in loose ground without essential timbering, then the Clerk of Works is to draw the contractor's attention to the matter and make a note in his diary that he has done so. If the contractor does not remedy the matter then the Clerk of Works is to report accordingly to the architect-in-charge.

13 Objects of antiquity

The Clerk of Works is to obtain from the Department a printed 'Reward' notice dealing with objects of antiquity found on the site and to arrange for the display of such notice in a prominent position during the periods of excavation. The Clerk of Works is to collect any objects of antiquity which may be found during the excavations and deliver them to the architect-in-charge. When such articles are located in excavations and are not easily movable, work on the spot and in the immediate vicinity is to be suspended and the architect-in-charge notified by telephone immediately, who will arrange for work to be renewed under special supervision. Immediately upon making a 'find' the Clerk of Works should, unless he is absolutely certain that it is of no interest, notify the Job Architect and Historic Buildings Division (Tel. 01-633-5868). Historic Buildings Division will arrange an early visit to the site or failing this give instructions as far as possible over the telephone. If an isolated object is brought to the Clerk of Works he should try to ascertain (and state in a report for HB Division) the depth and type of soil in which the buried object was found, with a sketch of the location in relation to the rest of the site. If the find or part of it is still undisturbed the Clerk of Works should immediately consult the Historic Buildings Division and isolate the relevant part of the site until the Historic Buildings Division inspection (which will be immediate) has been made. Any decision to isolate a part of a site which might lead to a claim by the contractor for delay, shall be the subject of an immediate report by Historic Buildings Division (in conjunction with the division concerned) to the executive Committee and the Planning Committee. Historic Buildings Division will take into care any isolated find. They will arrange, as a matter of immediate urgency for the inspection of finds where work on the site has been affected and will make recommendations to the executive division on any special arrangements which may be necessary for the uncovering or preservation of antiquities. If specialist supervision of such work is desirable the arrangements will be made by the executive division concerned on the advice of the Historic Buildings Division.

14 Cultivation of areas to be planted or grassed

Clerks of Works are to ensure that areas that are to be soiled, planted or grassed are properly cleared of debris and obstructions to the depths and in the manner laid down in the Specification; and Clerks of Works are to personally check that this work has been efficiently carried out.

15 Information

The following are useful sources of information on foundations:
1 Foundations and substructures. Code of Practice CP 101 : 1972 : below four storeys.
2 Foundations. Civil Engineering Code of Practice CP 2004 : 1972.
3 Soils and Foundations, BRS Digests Nos. 63, 64 and 67 (1965 and 1966).

GREATER LONDON COUNCIL

DEPARTMENT OF ARCHITECTURE AND CIVIC DESIGN

RECORDS OF GROUND CONDITIONS IN GREATER LONDON

Ref. AR/HO/SM   Date

Division   Site Location

Architect

Structural Eng.

Clerk of Works

Contractor

SUMMARY OF FOUNDATION DETAILS (AS EXECUTED)

Blk No and Type	No of Storeys	TYPE OF FOUNDATION (Inc. Width of Trenches and Depth of Concrete.)	Depth of Dig or Length of Piles		Type of Sub Soil on which Foundation Rests
			Min.	Max.	

Remarks—(e.g. Water trouble, strata penetrated, obstructions encountered).

2m (TJ 21371-B30036-814) 9.70

9 Drainage

1 Checking levels and locations of existing sewers

Where the proposed drains and sewers are to connect to an existing soil and/or surface water sewer the Clerk of Works is to check the location of these sewers against the drawings and is to check the levels of the existing sewers against the Benchmarks referred to in the specification. The Clerk of Works must also contact the Engineer of the Local Authority in whom the sewers are vested so that his staff may positively identify the sewers to which connection is to be made. All these checks are to be made before work on the proposed sewers and drains is started and the Clerk of Works is to inform the architect-in-charge immediately of any discrepancies.

2 Setting out

The Clerk of Works is to check the setting out of manhole and inspection chamber positions and the location of drainage runs before excavation is commenced. In particular he is to check that the distances between manholes and chambers correspond to those shown on the drawings. Any discrepancy in these distances must be reported to the architect-in-charge as differences in distance may require adjustments in invert levels to maintain satisfactory gradients. The Clerk of Works is also to check and record the levels of all pegs and site rails and the constructed levels of all manholes and inspection chambers as the work proceeds.

3 Excavations

The Clerk of Works is to inspect the bottoms of all drainage excavations before any pipes, concrete or granular beds are laid. Should he consider that the bottom of the excavation or any part of it is not suitable for the type of construction proposed he is to inform the architect-in-charge and obtain his approval to any work required additional to the contract. Such works may include the digging out of soft places and replacing with good material, the construction of land drains in the trench bottom to keep the excavations clear of water and possibly a change in the method of support proposed for the new drain or sewer. The Clerk of Works must also check and record the levels of all drainage excavation prior to the construction of the drainage works. The Clerk of Works is referred to Section 8 ' Foundations ' of this handbook where he will find a number of relevant provisions regarding the supervision of excavation works.

4 Support and protection of the proposed sewers and drains

The Clerk of Works is to ensure that the contract requirements regarding the support and protection of the proposed sewers and drains are complied with by the contractor and is to keep records, counter-signed and agreed by the contractor, of all concrete, granular or other materials provided by the contractor for the support and protection of the sewers and drains.

5	**Backfilling**	The Clerk of Works is to ensure that the specification requirements regarding backfilling are scrupulously observed. In particular it is important that filling immediately over pipes is carefully placed and that the remainder of the filling is thoroughly consolidated in layers and watered if necessary. Backfilling around manholes, particularly when these are located in roads or paved areas, must also be carefully compacted as described above. Proper consolidation of backfill is a job that is frequently skimped if not properly supervised and can lead to expensive reinstatement works at a later date.
6	**Timber left in**	Should the Clerk of Works consider that in order to preserve the stability of existing or proposed structures it is desirable to leave in certain sections of excavation timbering he should inform the architect-in-charge and obtain his authorisation. A record agreed by the contractor is to be kept of the amount and location of all timber left in.
7	**Testing of sewers and drains**	The Clerk of Works is referred to Section 21 'Testing', for information regarding the testing of sewers and drains.
8	**Connection to existing sewers**	Before making any connections to existing sewers the Clerk of Works is to contact the Engineer of the Local Authority in whom the sewers are vested to ascertain whether there are any particular requirements that must be observed. It may be found that the Local Authority insist on making the connection themselves in which case the Clerks of Works must co-ordinate this work with that of the contractor.
9	**Handing over of sewers and drains**	Before completion of a contract the Clerk of Works is to ensure by rodding that all drains are clear and free from obstructions and all drains are to be tested for soundness immediately prior to handing over. Before undertaking this work the Clerk of Works must contact the Public Health Inspector of the Local Authority to obtain details of the tests required by the Local Authority and to arrange for the Public Health Inspector to be present when the tests are carried out. The Clerk of Works must record in detail in his diary all tests of drains and should obtain a signed acceptance from the Public Health Inspector for all lengths of drain that are accepted by him as satisfactory.

10 Concrete and Reinforced Concrete

1 New Code of Practice 110

By a combination of various codes, relating to concrete, into a new Unified Code, a Code of Practice 110 entitled 'The Structural Use of Concrete' was introduced in November 1972.

With the complete omission of the classical elastic theory the theory of Limit States, which has international acceptance, has been developed and used in the new code, with statistical probability calculations being used for loads, strengths, and control checks.

The resultant Code of Practice 110 'The Structural Use of Concrete' is very much in advance of, and different from, anything of this type that has been produced before. Except for general background information this need not concern the Clerk of Works, but in the immediate future as the recommendations of the new Code of Practice are gradually absorbed by the industry some alterations in specification requirements and in the sophistication of construction methods and control will undoubtedly take place.

2 Developments

The possible future site control developments will certainly be of interest to the Clerk of Works, and in view of the present developing stage of structural concrete technique generally, it would be as well that a few definitions of practical interest should be given.

3 Types of Concrete

1 Ordinary Structural Concrete, produced by:
   (i)   Prescribed Mixes, or
   (ii) Designed Mixes, or
2 Special Structural Concrete, produced by:
   (i)   Prescribed Mixes, or
   (ii) Designed Mixes.

4 Definitions

1 *Ordinary Structural Concrete:*
Is in general terms, any grade of concrete made from Portland cement, natural aggregates and water.
2 *Special Structural Concrete:*
Is in general terms, concrete made with special cements, e.g., High Alumina, or with admixtures or special aggregates.
3 *Prescribed Mixes:*
Are in general terms what we have hitherto called nominal mixes. These are relatively rich in cement and are used when it is considered that the additional expense of establishing a designed mix and statistically controlling it by works cube tests, is not justified.
4 *Designed Mixes:*
Are mixes designed by the Contractor or his supplier to comply with the strength requirements demanded by the specification. To ensure an appropriate

durability, the minimum cement content and a nominal maximum size of aggregate will be stipulated. Unless specified otherwise it will be the Contractor's responsibility that the workability of the concrete is suitable for the particular handling and placing conditions.

The Contractor must:

(a) Demonstrate that the mix design is satisfactory by a series of trial mixes, or evidence of previous satisfactory use.

(b) Employ a technically qualified supervisor in charge of the concrete work.

(c) Maintain a comprehensive statistical control on the cube test results continuously during the progress of the concrete work.

5 Demonstration that designed mix achieves the appropriate surface finish

A point that the Clerk of Works should not overlook is that whilst the designed mix is being established to suit the constructional requirements of the contract, the contractor must also demonstrate that the designed mix will satisfactorily achieve the appropriate surface finish required by the architect-in-charge. The Clerk of Works should talk this feature over with the architect-in-charge and if necessary with the structural engineer.

6 Grades of Concrete

Grades of concrete are tested by 28 day strength in Newtons/mm², and the particular grades are chosen by the designer after consideration of the type of use, characteristic strength required and exposure conditions and cover provided.

7 The London Building Act

The London Building Act refers to nominal mixes for the various grades of concrete (opening the way for designed mixes in Table 10). A required minimum crushing strength for control purposes by means of works cube tests is stated in every case.

8 Departmental Preambles

The Departments standard preambles also quote nominal mix figures for the various grades of concrete but includes minimum cement content safeguards. If the contractor requests the substitution of designed mixes, the Department has full alternative specification instructions available in the preambles to introduce fully controlled designed mix techniques immediately these are required.

9 Proportioning Materials on Site

The Clerk of Works must note that, in whatever way concrete is specified, the actual proportioning of materials for making concrete on site, other than liquids, must be done by weight, and by no other means, unless special and particular approval is given otherwise.

In the translation of volumes to weights when required the Clerk of Works should consult the structural engineer.

10 Frequent test cubes

In designed mixes, as has been mentioned, the contractor is required to maintain continuous control by cube tests, the results of these being subject to statistical interpretation. The reason is, as the Clerk of Works will note, that the contractor has almost complete responsibility for the concrete mix, and the operations generally to produce the concrete.
It is therefore necessary for the site control to monitor very carefully and continuously the strengths of the concrete we are in fact getting from the contractor.

11 Calcium chloride in concrete

It is a Departmental Instruction that calcium chloride must NOT be used as an additive, either as calcium chloride or under any proprietary name, in any insitu or precast work containing reinforcement or embedded metals, where either

(i)   the concrete is exposed to the weather, or
(ii)   the concrete is exposed to damp conditions internally, or
(iii) the concrete is steam cured, or
(iv)   the cement is any other than Portland Cement or Rapid Hardening complying with BS 12, or
(v)   the concrete cover to any reinforcement or embedded metal is less than 1 inch (excluding any exposed aggregate), or
(vi)   the embedded metal projects from the concrete (e.g., stair case railings), or
(vii) the concrete is to be prestressed.

The use of calcium chloride additive is not called for in the Council's contract documents and its use is strictly permissive. Where contractors apply for permission to use calcium chloride, approval may only be given after consultation with the Structural Engineer.

12 Change in materials

With designed mixes, if a change is made in the materials or proportions, fresh trial mixes must be made.

13 Competent supervision by contractor

With designed mixes a contract requirement is that a named competent supervisor of adequate technical qualification, must supervise all stages in the preparation and placing of the concrete. If the Clerk of Works considers that this work is not in fact receiving adequate supervision he should bring this to the immediate attention of both the Structural Engineer and architect-in-charge.
If due to this inadequacy the results of control test cubes are doubtful then when the interpretation of the results

of the test cubes are made by the Structural Engineer, he will advise the architect-in-charge of the recommended course of action, both technically and for future concrete supervision.

14 Ready mixed concrete —choice of depot

A good deal of concrete used on sites today is delivered to site ready mixed.
Should a contractor wish to use ready mixed concrete he will usually be required to make written application stating from which firm and depot the concrete will be supplied.
The architect-in-charge will consult the Officer i/c Testing Station who will vet the supplying firm and the specific depot proposed, and advise the architect-in-charge of his recommendation.

15 Minimum cement content—ready mixed concrete

For ready mixed concrete the minimum cement content should be marked on the ticket for each ready mixed delivery.
This is a most important requirement because it is possible to produce a concrete in which the cement content, although sufficient to produce the required strength, is insufficient to produce the required durability.
The Clerk of Works should normally refuse to accept deliveries of ready mixed concrete where the cement content is below the amount specified, or is not marked on the ticket, and should consult the Structural Engineer on the matter.

16 Careful check of ready mixed concrete by Clerk of Works

Ready mixed concrete requires a careful check by the Clerk of Works, including the regular taking of slump tests as well as the regular taking of test cubes.
The concrete must comply with Clauses 5 and 6 of BS 1926, but in all other respects with the Department's requirements.

17 Check of delivery times —ready mixed concrete

The Clerk of Works should additionally check the delivery ticket to see that the concrete is being delivered within the period specified in BS 1926 which for a truck mixer or agitator is within two hours, or for non-agitating delivery equipment is within one hour of mixing.

18 Disclosure of additives

The supplying firm must make 'disclosure to the Council' of any additives that have been incorporated in the mix, and of the brand of cement used.

19 Mixing concrete on site

The Clerk of Works should check the weighing accuracy of the mixing plant before concreting

commences and thereafter every morning when concreting is in progress.
A convenient way of doing this is by using bags of cement as check weights.
All mixers must be fitted with water gauges which must be maintained in good order. It is advisable to check that the water gauge is accurate by measuring the quantity of water actually entering the drum when the mixer is running. This check should be made at the beginning of the job, and occasionally thereafter, and whenever the mixer is moved.
If the aggregates are wet, an adjustment should be made to the quantity of the mixing water.

20 Materials for concreting on site

The Clerk of Works is to ensure that the fine and coarse aggregates are satisfactory in grading, quality and cleanliness, in accordance with the specification and are stored on a clean hard standing with the fine aggregate separated from the coarse aggregate by a suitable partition. The Clerk of Works is also to satisfy himself that the cement is fresh, is stored satisfactorily off the ground in a damp proof shed, and that the contractor uses the cement in reasonable rotation of deliveries.

21 Marine aggregates

When marine aggregates are being used in either ready-mix or site mixed concrete, the Clerk of Works should make arrangements to visit the suppliers' depot and supervise the taking of aggregate samples (both fine and coarse) for submission to the Testing Station at County Hall (see Section 21, item 12).
The frequency of testing will be agreed between the architect, the officer-in-charge of the Testing Station and the Clerk of Works prior to the commencement of the contract.

22 Gauge Boxes

If, very unusually, volume batching is permitted the Clerk of Works must personally check the gauge boxes, and in use make due allowance for the ' bulking ' of sand, the size of gauge boxes being such that a complete bag of cement can be used with each mixing.

23 Mixer size

The use of a mixer much bigger than necessary for the mix regularly used (for example the use of a 14/10 mixer for a one bag 1 :2 :4 mix) should be discouraged as far as is practical, as with this practice there is a tendency for the mix to be overloaded with aggregate when supervision is inadequate.

24 Formwork

The Clerk of Works must satisfy himself of the adequacy of the formwork, as to line and level, tightness of joints, strength against deflection and smoothness of surface.

The Clerk of Works should check that the mould oil used is reasonable, that the Contractor does not build his formwork so that parts of it are trapped during the striking operation, that side forms of beams may be struck without disturbing beam bottoms. On such similar matters borne of experience, the Clerk of Works could well advise the agent or shuttering foreman to mutual benefit.

25 Cleaning out Formwork

Cleaning out of formwork should be done before the positioning of formwork makes access difficult or impossible; and a final check should be made by the Clerk of Works immediately prior to concreting. If the formwork is cleaned by blowing out with compressed air, the Clerk of Works must ensure that, for example the floor rubbish is not blown into the boxed out column shuttering where it can do the greatest damage. This sort of thing is far from being unusual.

26 Placing of concrete

The Clerk of Works must ensure that the provisions of the specification with regard to placing concrete are correctly observed, particularly with regard to: placing in cold weather; placing without segregation; placing before concrete has become too stiff to be efficiently compacted; prevention of disturbance to reinforcement during placing; very thorough compaction either by vibration, tamping or rodding; prevention of disturbance to the concrete after placing and compaction.

A Clerk of Works will often find it necessary to consult with the contractor as to what will constitute a day's work, so that construction joints if found necessary, occur in the appropriate position, and the contractor is not for example caught out by darkness part way across a bay.

27 Construction joints

There is another important aspect of construction joints, as well as determining the days output. The structural engineer may have reservations regarding the location of construction joints in certain vulnerable structural positions, while the architect-in-charge will be concerned that joints exposed to view will not adversely affect the appearance of the building. It should be realised that it is virtually impossible either to form a joint that cannot be seen or to avoid a variation in tone between one casting to the next.

For these reasons, before any important pour of concrete, the Clerk of Works should check the proposed position of the construction joints with both the structural engineer and the architect-in-charge.

28 Concreting in cold weather

Unless special measures are taken no concreting should normally be permitted by the Clerk of Works when the atmospheric temperature is below 3°C, or where the temperature of the concrete cannot be maintained at 3°C or above throughout the placing, curing and hardening periods.

No frozen or frosted aggregate should be permitted to be used on any account.

Where the contractor proposes to take special measures either by the use of admixtures, special cements and/or heating of the materials, the Clerk of Works should not give permission for these on his own account but should refer to the architect-in-charge for his instructions.

For the guidance of a Clerk of Works it should be noted that the use of admixtures alone (or special cements) is of very little practical use without special pre-heating; shielding and post-heating precautions.

Concreting, especially of suspended reinforced work, will therefore not be permitted in freezing weather where the contractor proposes to use the admixture alone.

A maximum and minimum thermometer will be supplied by the Council for the use of the Clerk of Works, and a jacketed concreting thermometer will be supplied by the contractor as part of the normal concreting equipment, and may be called for as required. In frosty weather the Clerk of Works should record external temperature in his diary and in his weekly report.

29 Compaction of Concrete

The presence of 5% voids in concrete can reduce its strength by 30% and very considerably reduce its durability. It is therefore essential for the Clerk of Works to ensure that all concrete is thoroughly compacted under the direct supervision of a competent member of the contractor's staff.

Where immersion vibrators are used they should be inserted vertically at not greater distance than about 500 mm apart, and withdrawn very slowly when air bubbles no longer come to the surface.

Vibrators should not be used to move concrete laterally as this causes segregation, nor should they be brought too close to the formwork where sand runs may be created.

Particular attention should be given to vibration at the top of a lift, e.g., in a column or wall.

30 Curing and protection

Proper curing and protection of the concrete in accordance with the specification is of the utmost importance. Unless the Clerk of Works maintains a

43

firm watchfulness on this matter right from the beginning the operatives may tend at the end of the day's work to carry out the curing and protective measures in a perfunctory and inefficient manner.
The Clerk of Works should therefore take care to see that a good routine is firmly established.
Concrete that will be exposed to air (and in particular concrete having a high class finish) must be protected from damage to arrises or face and from being disfigured by grout, or other droppings, or staining from standing scaffolding or reinforcement.

31 High alumina cement

The policy of the Greater London Council on the use of high alumina cement is specified in Information Note 13/74 dated September 1974 and is as follows:
'The use of high alumina cement for structural purposes including foundation work is PROHIBITED until further notice unless specifically recommended by the Structural Engineering Division'.
All reference to high alumina cement concrete has been deleted from the Code of Practice CP 110 Part 1, 1972 by Amendment No. 1 dated August 1974.
In addition to the above, the London Building (Constructional) Amending Bylaws 1974 came into force on 1 July 1975. These bylaws prohibit the use of high alumina cement for structural work without the prior approval of the Council.
If high alumina concerte is specified care is required:

(i)   No trace of other cements or limes should be left on plant or tools used for making or handling high alumina concrete. If high alumina cement is allowed to come into contact with cement of a different type a ' flash set ' will take place.

(ii) All formwork should be watertight and saturated in water when the high alumina concrete is placed.

(iii) All formwork and props must be left in position for a minimum period of 24 hours.
In frosty weather this period must be extended by the number of days during which the temperature is at freezing point or below.

(iv) Lifts of concrete in mass should not exceed 300 mm and time should be allowed for the heat to dissipate, the next lift not being poured for 12 hours after the first.

(v)   The evolution of heat from high alumina cement concrete is considerable, particularly between 6 hours and 12 hours after mixing, and to prevent ' dry-out ' it is essential that the Clerk of Works ensures that the work is kept thoroughly wet, and covers and formwork saturated for 24 hours.

High alumina cement concrete should not be mixed or placed if the temperature at the point of placing is liable to be over 27°C. It is a matter of some interest that high alumina cement concrete, even after the initial curing, can be seriously affected by continuous exposure to hot (over 27°C) and wet conditions. In addition it is thought that high alumina cement mixtures can be adversely affected by alkalis.

32 Reinforcement

The Clerk of Works must see that the provisions of the specification with regard to steel bending, fixing, and placing, are carefully and accurately, carried out. He must check in considerable detail that every bar is of correct size and length, is properly scaled and clean, is correctly bent, is in correct position laterally and vertically, has proper cover, and is securely wired with tying wire. The Clerk of Works should make this detailed check of the reinforcement with the detail drawings out on the site of work, before the engineer's or District Surveyor's inspection and before permission to place concrete is given. BS 1478 gives guidance on bending dimensions.

As the top reinforcement in a balcony is usually light, very considerable care has to be taken that the contractor adequately supports the steel and does not in any way displace it when concreting. For this reason it is required that the Clerk of Works (unless specially relieved by the Resident Engineer) personally sees the placing of every bit of concrete on all such balconies under his supervision, and carefully and personally ascertains that the steel reinforcement is correctly in position and remains so.

At the same time as checking the reinforcement, the Clerk of Works is to see that the formwork, particularly beam and column pockets, is properly cleaned out and that electricity and similar conduits are firmly secured in their correct positions.

33 Provision for pipes

Cutting away of reinforced concrete work is not to be permitted without the special prior consent of the architect-in-charge or engineer. For this reason a very careful check must be made by the Clerk of Works before the concreting operation is commenced that all plumbing, heating pipes, etc., are properly set in position or that proper provision is made for them, in accordance with the specification, by boxings or other specified method.

34 Striking of formwork

A Clerk of Works will often receive pressing requests from a contractor for permission to strike formwork earlier than the specified times, with various reasons given. On no account whatsoever must the Clerk of Works on his own responsibility permit the reduction of the specified striking times, even to a very limited extent. Only by specific and definite instructions from the architect-in-charge or the structural engineer may any such reduction be allowed, and in practice permission for this will rarely be given.

35 Damaged or defective work in general

In the case of damaged or defective concrete, in particular work affecting the surface finishes, the architect-in-charge will direct as to whether the work is to be entirely renewed, or may be rectified. On specially textured surfaces where any such rectification work depends on the ability of a making-good craftsman to match the existing work, then it is necessary that the remedial work be undertaken immediately. Excuses for postponing the remedial work should not be accepted. If in fact the contractor does procrastinate in the remedial work required on any concrete surface, the Clerk of Works is to report the circumstance in writing to the architect-in-charge, and, in the Housing Branch, to the Sites Manager, so that appropriate action can be taken. The circumstances should also be noted in the 'General Observations' column of the Clerk of Works Weekly Report.
This applies to surface defects of any kind, and includes badly made construction joints.

36 Specified surface finishes

Any specification requirements relating to surface finish, must, as befits an architect's department, be strictly observed.
Matters relating to particular types of finish are as follows:

1 *Smooth faced concrete surfaces to be painted:*
The formwork should be struck as early as permitted by the specification and at the discretion of the Clerk of Works minor defects such as small air holes may be made good by rubbing down the *whole* surface with the planed end grain of a block of wood and a limited amount of water. It is preferable that no cement or sand be added during the course of this operation, provided that enough 'fat' can be worked up from the original work. The use of a steel trowel should be prohibited under all circumstances. Work with greater imperfections should be brought to the attention of the architect-in-charge, and no remedial work should be attempted until he has inspected the work and agreed to the proposed remedial method.

2 *Smooth-faced surfaces to be left unpainted:*
These should satisfy the standard for painted work described above with the additional requirement that

the work should as far as possible be of even colour. Since it is impossible to avoid variations in tone between one pour and another, individual members should be completed in one pour wherever possible. Any making good other than rubbing down (without sand and cement) will inevitably show and mar the appearance, and for that reason should seldom be undertaken, and then only after the agreement of the architect-in-charge.

Minor defects in their original state will frequently prove to be less noticeable than the results of attempts to make good.

Where some making good is considered, in agreement with the architect-in-charge, to be unavoidable, consideration should be given to the incorporation of a proportion of white cement in the repair mix to avoid the darker tone usually associated with repair patches. Patched areas should be kept moist for several days, and the repairs should be carried out by a skilled craftsman.

3 *Exposed Aggregate Finishes:*
The Clerk of Works should check that the full cover of reinforcement is obtained, bearing in mind that in the surface operation some small amount of material may be removed from the concrete face.

Bush hammered surfaces will usually incorporate an untooled margin as it is not practicable to work close to the edge of a member without damaging the arris. Tools of unequal sharpness should not be used on the same panel.

37 Colour

Where it is specified, or directed, that certain parts of the work shall be executed in concrete having a uniform colour it is important that the Clerk of Works ensures that all the cement supplied for that work is obtained from the same source, and that the contractor has informed the manufacturer of the requirement for uniformity of colour.

The Clerk of Works must also check that the sand supplied for such work is of uniform colour and remove any that fails to match the approved sample.

He must also ensure that the water content of each mix is constant as a small variation will lead to a change in colour and tone. It is also important that there should be no variations in the mix proportions particularly with regard to the ratio of cement to aggregates.

38 Vertical alignment and setting out in multi-storey reinforced concrete work

It is notoriously difficult without skill and care for construction gangs to maintain strict accuracy of the vertical alignment and the horizontal setting out of all the structural reinforced concrete multi-storey members, walls, floors, columns and beams in high rise work; but the very best of care must be taken by the Clerk of Works to see that such accuracy is in fact obtained by the contractor throughout his work, and stipulated tolerances not exceeded.

This must of necessity involve accuracy check measurements at regular intervals; either by the Clerk of Works; or by a special team as part of a Quality Control programme; or by the contractor carrying out specified accuracy measurements under appropriately skilled engineer control, using steel tape, level, theodolite and autoplumb as required in the presence of, and recorded by, the Clerk of Works, to demonstrate that the appropriate accuracy has been obtained.

This is of particular importance in the case, for example, of brickwork skin cladding the reinforced concrete structured multi-storey buildings where brickwork skins ledge on concrete nibs, and therefore the maintenance of a strict accuracy in the basic reinforced concrete structure is absolutely essential.

39 Clerk of Works to seek instructions on accuracy measurements that are to be taken

The arrangements to be made will be laid down by the architect-in-charge advised by the structural engineer before the contract begins; and where a Clerk of Works has a tall block contract or any contract where the accuracy check measurements, that it is necessary to take, form a fairly extensive programme, then the Clerk of Works should make it his business to take instructions in the matter, at the beginning of the contract from his architect-in-charge.

40 Designed Mixes—Field Control Samples and Test Cubes

For field control checks of designed mixes, apart entirely from the trial mixes originally made to determine the design of the mixes, the following samples of concrete are to be taken:

1 A sample of the mixes on eight separate occasions during each of the first five days of using a particular grade of concrete.

2 Thereafter at least one sample on each day that particular grade of concrete is made.

If the cement in the mix is Portland cement two cubes are to be made from each sample, one 7 day and one 28 days.

If the cement is High Alumina one cube is to be made from each sample for one day test.

The Clerk of Works will note that this means 80 test cubes in the first five days for Portland Cement concrete with two cubes each day thereafter; and 40 test cubes in the first five days for High Alumina cement with one cube each day thereafter.

The Clerk of Works should remember that Field Control cube strengths are to be the subject of a continuous statistical check during the whole of the work with a designed mix.

41 Nominal or Prescribed Mixes—Field Control Samples and Test Cubes

For field control checks of nominal or prescribed mixes three separate samples shall be taken from placed material at the time of concreting.
In the case of Portland Cement each sample is to provide one 7 day and one 28 day cube i.e., 6 cubes in all, for each concreting operation.
In the case of High Alumina each sample is to provide one cube for test at the age of one day, i.e., 3 cubes in all, for each concreting operation.

42 B.S. references for sampling, slump and cubes

The Method of Making Test Cubes is fully detailed in British Standard 1881. Part 3. 1970.
The Method of Making a Slump Test is fully detailed in British Standard 1881. Part 2. 1970.
The Method of Sampling Fresh Concrete is fully detailed in British Standard 1881. Part 1. 1970,
and all these British Standards, with others, form part of the British Standards in the permanent issue set for Clerks of Works.

43 Covermeter checks

Covermeter checks for steel positioning on parts such as cantilever balconies and spanning stair flights, are mandatory, the features to be checked being decided in advance by the architect-in-charge in cooperation with the superintendent of works, with, if necessary, structural engineer guidance. These are to be recorded.

11 Brickwork

1 Setting out of brickwork

The setting out of the brickwork is to be checked by the Clerk of Works with relation to the established centre line of the building and the given ' building line '. All dimensional checks should be made with a steel tape. Regular checks should be made as the work rises. The Clerk of Works, who must thoroughly familiarise himself with the brickbond specified, is to check that the setting out of the first course of ' neat work ' is accurately and intelligently done so that irregular or broken bond is avoided and the cutting of bricks reduced to a minimum.

2 Datum for brickwork

The Clerk of Works is to check that the bricklayers are working from proper datum levels either pegged and protected or incised on walls or columns.
A convenient basic datum is the finished floor level (FFL) of the ground floor.
The Clerk of Works should strongly encourage the use of storey rods which should set out storey heights in relation to site datum level, and show heights of tops and bottoms of openings, course levels, and other features. The use of storey rods is now a specified requirement and the Clerk of Works is to familiarise himself with the clause concerned.

3 Damp-proof courses

The Clerk of Works is to see that the course upon which the damp-proof material is laid is carefully flushed up with mortar to an even bed, and the damp-proof material laid and protected from injury while the mortar is setting.

4 Points for attention in brickwork

In ensuring that the provisions of the specification with regard to bricklaying workmanship are observed the Clerk of Works should pay personal attention to the following:
1 That the correct bricks to match the specified coursing, and metric or imperial, as specified are on the scaffold.
2 Adequate and correct damp proofing.
3 Flushing up of bed joints and filling of collar and cross joints; bricks frog up.
4 Correct brick coursing, with correct course alignment, and the keeping of true perpends.
5 Correct wall ties, correctly set and correctly spaced.
6 Proper raking out of joints for subsequent pointing.
7 Cleanliness of all cavities and the correct use of cleaning out holes, and cavity battens.
8 Correct cavity gap dimensions.
9 Accuracy in dimensions of openings, and adequate and correct frame fixing.
10 Accurate provision of sleeves and chases for services.

11 Protection of features, finished stair treads, and cast stone work as soon as built.
12 Protection and cleanliness of finished brickwork; including protection from scaffold staining and from splashing off scaffold boards (the inner of which should be turned back during rain).

5 Particular attention to cavity brickwork

With the very much increased use of irregular labour-only bricklaying gangs, particular attention needs to be paid by the Clerk of Works to the regular and proper supervision on his part of all cavity brickwork. Considerable troubles have occurred on sites due to slipshod workmanship in cavity work; and considerable expense in subsequent repair has been incurred. If a Clerk of Works in charge of brickwork is not quite certain, from the evidence of his own eyes, that in every part of his cavity brickwork he has the correct wall tie type, correctly positioned, fully bedded onto each leaf, with the correct width of cavity, and positive cavity cleanliness, he is not doing his duty; and he must take immediate steps to see that he takes a controlling position in this work. He should take this position, with aid from his Superintendent of Works, and from his Job Architect, regardless of objections from the contractor, or walk-offs by irregular bricklaying gangs or other difficulties.

Slipshod work in a trade of structural significance such as bricklaying is such a serious matter, that timely and strong steps must be taken to see that it does not occur in this department's work.

6 Weep holes

If weep holes are not specifically indicated in any type of cavity work the Clerk of Works should obtain instructions from the architect-in-charge. It will be normal for weep holes to be left at every fourth vertical joint in the external wall at the bottom of the cavity, and over openings.

7 Closure of cavity

Special attention should be given that the closing of the cavity at sides and head is correct to detail shown on drawing.

8 Snap headers

In cavity walls not in stretcher bond ' snap headers ' are often a source of trouble; care should be taken that these are cut neither too long nor too short, and if not particularly specified the use of purpose-made snap headers (as distinct from those cut on the scaffold) should be encouraged.

9 Mortar mixing

It is a specified requirement that all mortar materials shall be accurately gauged by gauge boxes and mechanically mixed. Particularly with calculated brick-work, the Clerk of Works must ensure that the methods the contractor uses for production of mortar for his bricklaying gangs does in fact produce, with adequate accuracy, a mortar of the proportions specified. Retempering is not permitted.

10 Pointing

The finish of brickwork mortar joints may be
Flush
Flush ironed
Weathered
Keyed
Recessed
and which one is to be used is specified for each type of facing brick.
Where pointing is required this is also specified.

11 Sample brick panels

The Contractor should be instructed by the Clerk of Works to produce sample panels of brickwork jointed and pointed for the approval of the architect-in-charge. Particular attention should be paid by the Clerk of Works during pointing operations subsequently to ensure that the approved method, colour and texture, are absolutely matched and maintained, without any variations between different portions of the work.

12 Sample loads of bricks

The first sample load of bricks that is accepted and approved by the architect-in-charge should be retained, until completion of all brickwork deliveries to enable the quality and appearance of all subsequent deliveries to be judged.

13 Brickwork in frosty weather

In cold weather, as a protection against night and early morning frosts the Clerk of Works is to see that newly erected brickwork is properly covered. Stacks of bricks on site should also be covered and if the contractor omits this precaution the Clerk of Works should not allow the use of frosted over bricks.

14 Admixtures

Contractors are prone to request permission to use admixtures alone, in the mortar, to protect against frost, rather in the form of a prophylactic.
The use of admixtures alone, without special covering and heating measures, is of very little practical use for the mortar usually specified.
Permission should not therefore be given for load bearing brickwork to be built in freezing weather, when the contractor proposes using admixtures alone.
With proper heating and covering measures, however, brickwork can usually proceed, and if the contractor puts

up detailed proposals for this, then they should be referred to the architect-in-charge for his approval.

15 Examination of brickwork built in frost	Where brickwork has been built in freezing weather the work should be given a special examination by the Clerk of Works the second day after being built. If there is no obvious frost damage but the work is suspect, portions should be tested with a blow lamp; if the mortar softens frost action has most certainly affected the work which must be rebuilt.
16 Sills and thresholds	The Clerk of Works should see that continuous sills and thresholds built in as the work proceeds are bedded only at the stoolings to prevent fracture at settlement, the open joint being subsequently filled with mortar.
17 Partition blocks	The Clerk of Works is to see that lightweight, clinker, concrete blocks for partitions are given all reasonable possible protection against rain or frost, are stacked off the ground, with reasonable facilities for air circulation, and when used in the work are dry and adequately matured.
18 Tests during brickwork	The Clerk of Works is to obtain instructions from the architect-in-charge relating to the testing of materials used in brickwork. It will be normal for the following tests to be carried out: 1 Crushing tests for bricks for designated brickwork. 2 Porosity tests on facings. 3 Strength tests on partition blocks where brands in use have not been recently tested and given general approval. 4 Mortar tests. 5 Breaking tests on a percentage of precast concrete steps. Details of a Clerk of Works duties in connection with the forwarding of samples for testing, to the Council's Testing Station, are given in the Section of these instructions entitled 'TESTING'.
19 Flues	Very special attention is to be paid to ensuring that all flue linings are fixed socket upwards, are properly jointed in sulphate resisting mortar as specified and have a solid and continuous backing. All flues are to be tested by the Contractor in the presence of the Clerk of Works who is to forward a certificate to the department, at the completion of each portion of the work that the flues have been tested in accordance with the specification and found clear. The Clerk of Works should also record the date of the tests in his Job Diary. The Clerk of Works should ensure that flues are cored as

the work proceeds, coring holes being left where necessary; coring should not be delayed until the chimney is complete.

20 Making good to ducts and other party structures

The Clerk of Works is to examine the making good of all holes in ducts, especially under baths, or in similar awkward positions, so that there is no possibility of mice getting into dwellings via ducts or from one dwelling to another where these are connected to the same duct. Such cases have occurred. If there is any potential weakness, where such infestation might be likely to occur, the Clerk of Works is to draw this to the attention of the architect-in-charge.

21 Records that are to be kept of all cavity and similar brickwork

It is most important that records of cavity and similar brickwork completed section by section, and floor by floor are personally recorded by the Clerk of Works. A record should be made before each sealing of temporary cleaning out holes.
This recording by the Clerk of Works indicates that he personally has satisfied himself that each section of the brickwork has the specified number of the correct ties, correctly positioned, fully bedded onto each leaf, with the outer leaf (if applicable) correctly ledged on to the concrete nib, with the correct width of cavity and positive cavity cleanliness, and that the section of the work has been completed in full accord with good practice and the specification concerned.

22 Manner in which records are to be kept

Normally these records will be kept in chart form on elevational drawings (similarly to records of concrete poured) and must be readily available to the architect-in-charge and other inspecting officers.
At the commencement of the brickwork on the contract the detailed supervision of the work, and the manner in which records must be kept are to be discussed by the Clerk of Works with his superintendent of works. These instructions apply to all cavity brickwork, including where single skin brickwork is used to clad concrete columns or walls with anchors to slots being used as the fixing method.

23 Cladding panels

Where cladding panels are used the Clerk of Works must make similar arrangements for the detailed supervision of the positioning and fixing of each panel, and the method of recording this, with his superintendent of works.

24 Cracking of brickwork and failures of brick cladding

During the last ten years there have been a number of cases of cracking, brick slip damage, spalling, and movement of half-brick skins to buildings, mainly multi-storey reinforced concrete framed buildings where concrete shrinkage, and creep, are factors, not usually involving major structural failure, but involving the danger of parts of brickwork falling and endangering the public below.

Some Clerks of Works consider it something of an enigma that these failures of brickwork cladding should occur on work built during the last ten or twelve years, but seemingly not in earlier work. It is a matter for thought, but it could well be that the comparative flexibility, and fragility, of modern half-brick outer skins, sometimes ledged onto concrete nibs, in contrast to earlier sturdier, if less efficient, designs, demands a precision of tolerance, and a workmanship accuracy and thoroughness not always forthcoming. It is not unknown that the tying of an outer skin of brickwork by wall-ties or anchors, might be somewhat less than perfectly carried out by bricklayers working under the stress of modern bonus conditions.

Nor has the necessity for appropriate movement joints in half-brick cladding been fully appreciated, or incorporated in designs where the risk of differential expansion, or shrinkage, is present.

These are all points to be noted very seriously by each Clerk of Works, in connection with the designs to which he is working. Any points of difficulty, or doubt, which he has should be discussed as necessary with his architect-in-charge.

25 Code of Practice C.P. 121

The Code of Practice C.P. 121, Part 1, for Walling, published in 1973 should be thoroughly read by each Clerk of Works, in particular the sections on ' Methods to reduce the incidence of cracking in brickwork and blockwork '. The basic principles contained in these sections should be studied, and understood, by all Clerks of Works.

HO.174

Greater London Council

DEPARTMENT OF ARCHITECTURE AND CIVIC DESIGN

HOUSING AND TOWN DEVELOPMENT BRANCH

Record of Flue Testing

Site or Estate _____

Block _____

Contractor _____

Dwelling number	Result of test of flues				Initials	Date
	Living room	1st bedroom	Any other flues			

CERTIFICATE

All the flues in the dwellings listed above have been tested and found clear.

(sgd.) _____

Clerk of Works.

56

12 Stress Grading of Timber

1 Code of Practice CP 112

This refers to structural timber, as distinct from joinery timber. The use of timber structurally is governed by British Code of Practice CP 112 (1971) and BS 4978 which have been prepared primarily for the guidance of engineers, and it is the department's structural engineers who will issue instructions and working rules in the matter, for example timber roof trusses, and the stress grading, machine or visual, of the timber concerned.

2 Stress Grading

Stress grading of timber simply means the assessment of the strength of the timber, and the reduction in the basic strength necessary because of defects such as knots, sloping grain, shakes and splits, or other imperfections and variations that one meets in a natural material such as timber.

3 Methods of Grading

1 VISUAL GRADING
Graders examine the timber visually guided by Appendix A of Code of Practice CP 112 and the rules laid down in BS 4978, and make their assessment of the timber grade. This is clearly a most uncertain method, depending on the experience, and the caution, of the graders, who can vary on occasion, in rejection figures, by up to 25%. In addition there are very few qualified graders in the Country and as a consequence visual grading is virtually never properly carried out.
2 MACHINE GRADING
Machine stress grading measures a relative ' stiffness ' and therefore strength, of the timber under test, the stiffness of timber being taken to be a fairly reliable indication of timber strength.
This stiffness is measured non-destructively by a Computermatic Stress Grading Machine, the timber passing through this machine at a fast rate, and depending on the deflection of each section, measured by computer, the timber is colour marked indicating its relative strength. The strength grade is then the lowest marking on the length of timber being tested.
This is naturally a very much better comparison method than the varied visual assessments of the differing grading personnel. There are however only a few machines in the country at the moment (Spring 1973) and until industry equips itself with machines they could not fully cope with the amounts of timber requiring stress grading.

4 Limitations of Machine Stress Grading

Machine stress grading has certain limitations inasmuch as there are certain specific defects not revealed by the machine testing process, and therefore it will be necessary for the Clerk of Works to visually inspect machine graded timber for compliance with specification requirements in respect of these defects. The defects concerned are wormholes, sapwood, fungal decay, brittle heart, bow and twist, fissures, resin pockets and wane. Where of course the reduction of strength caused by the defect is less than that caused by the defect admitted by the grade of timber then the piece of timber examined may be accepted.

It may be necessary however for the Clerk of Works to take advice from the Structural Engineer on the valuation of these defects and the treatments that may be necessary to neutralise these defects, pending the issue of rules for ' The Visual examination of Machine Stress Graded Timber for Structural Use ' which is to be included in the Preambles as an Appendix to a new Clause NI.4.

5 Colour Coding in Machine Grading

There is no British Standard colour code for machine stress graded timber. BS 4978 states that each piece of machine stress graded timber shall be stamped with the BS Kite Mark giving details of grade, licence number of grading machine, etc.

Licensees of the British Standards Institute Kite Mark Scheme tend to follow the recommendations given below with regard to colour coding:

M75 Grade—red
M50 Grade—blue
MSS Grade—purple
MGS Grade—green.

Reject timber is usually unmarked.

13 Joinery

1 Timber

For most of the housing joinery of the Department softwood is used, the more expensive hardwood being used in special situations only, and for high quality work; of the softwoods, Baltic Redwood is most often used at the moment, usually purchased by the joinery manufacturer in the grade ' unsorted '.

2 Timber windows

It is departmental policy that timber windows, in accordance with Branch details are to be used in all dwellings, except in special cases where express approval is given for aluminium windows.

3 Quality of timber

In late years the quality of timber in softwood joinery offered by the joinery manufacturers has in very many cases deteriorated and has not met the full and proper requirements of the department's specifications. The Clerk of Works is often placed in difficulty in this matter, being usually under pressure to accept the joinery as delivered, and therefore uncertain how to advise his Job Architect on such acceptance or otherwise. The Clerk of Works must, in every case, observe the correct procedure, as given later herein for the proper detailed and thorough inspection of the joinery.

4 Early decay of timber

Recently early breakdown of timber in external joinery has occurred so often and become so serious that alarm has been felt, not least by Clerks of Works. In 1969 the Scientific Adviser noted in his annual report to the Council that 'A substantial amount of failure has occurred on some Council sites through rotting of the sapwood of external joinery.

5 Early occurrence of wet-rot

The extensive failures that have occurred have usually been due to wet-rot occasioned by sapwood in softwood joinery timber being permeated by moisture, the amount of this moisture that gets into the untreated sapwood, and the readiness with which it gets in, in fact determining the life of the joinery component. It is the Clerk of Works duty to take such care in the inspection, installation and protection of joinery, in particular external softwood joinery, that any such early decay does not occur.

6 Moisture

It must be reiterated for emphasis, that while temperature and moisture control the movement behaviour of timber, moisture content is the governing factor in the suitability of timber for building; and the penetration of moisture into the vulnerable sapwood is the prime cause of decay.

7 Sapwood in softwood

The sapwood in softwood timber such as Swedish

Redwood, readily absorbs moisture and has very little resistance to decay. Nevertheless to take the logical course and to strictly specify that all softwood timber for external joinery shall be completely free from sapwood and to have that specification satisfactorily filled, has not proved to be commercially practicable.

Therefore in joinery for low-cost housing it is necessary to use softwood, knowing it has a vulnerable sapwood content, which unless treated, and protected, is likely to lead to early decay and breakdown.

8 Sapwood in hardwood

When hardwoods in usual use contain sapwood this is perishable, and not only this but both the sapwood and the heartwood are resistant to treatment with preservatives. Therefore where hardwoods are chosen for external joinery it should be stipulated that the hardwood should have no sapwood content, and the Clerk of Works should look for this during inspections.

9 Measures to be taken with softwood in present day use

Under circumstances such as these where timber containing sapwood and having little resistance to decay has necessarily to be used it is essential:—

1 To increase the resistance to decay artificially; and this is done by preservative treatment.

2 To accept only timber adequately seasoned and at the appropriate moisture content before being made into joinery and at time of delivery to site, and

3 To maintain the finished joinery at all times at the appropriate moisture content and to fully protect it from the ingress of moisture, which means: fully covered storage; no open joints; full and complete gluing of all joints with the right glue; no unprotected end grain; early and effective priming and painting; adequate putty work, paint covered; and, naturally, full and proper maintenance.

10 Preservation

It should be noted that British Standard 1186, which is based on a draft prepared by the British Woodwork Manufacturers Association, representing trade interests, makes no mention of preservation, except in so far as the added notes at the foot of Appendix A, page 11, refer to Code of Practice CP 153.

Both the British Standard, and the Code of Practice, are standard issues to Clerks of Works and should be studied.

Clerks of Works are to note that departmental policy now directs the use of preservation for all external joinery (other than ply-faced doors).

Preservation for external softwood, is to be by one of the following systems:

1 Boron diffusion

2 Double-vacuum impregnation
3 Automatically controlled immersion for a minimum
  period of three minutes.

**11 Moisture content
of joinery as delivered
on site**

The moisture content of timber in joinery, during manufacture, and when it arrives on site should be approximately 17% for external joinery and approximately 15% for internal joinery for buildings with intermittent heating.
The Clerk of Works should check, and record, the moisture content, using a moisture meter, as soon as joinery arrives on site, as part of the joinery inspection routine. A moisture meter is available from the Sites Managers' Office.

**12 Maintenance of low
moisture content**

A great deal of responsibility devolves on the Clerk of Works to see that joinery, after delivery to site, and until the building is handed over to the client's department and taken into service, receives proper protection, both in storage, and as far as may be possible during installation, so that the moisture content of the timber remains reasonably within the appropriate limits. Under the arduous conditions on site this will mean constant vigilance on the part of the Clerk of Works to see that the joinery is efficiently stored, fully covered and adequately protected at all times.

**13 Special steps for
centrally heated buildings**

Special steps may have to be taken in specification instructions to the main contractor and for his joinery manufacturer for the maturing and kiln drying of timber; and special steps in protective measures may also have to be taken on site when the joinery is for centrally heated buildings, or is to be used in constant heat positions.
If the necessary procedures are not dealt with in the specification then the Clerk of Works should request instructions, at the beginning of the contract, from his architect-in-charge.

14 Moisture danger limit

It is considered that the decay safety limit of air seasoned softwood, in equilibrium with its surroundings, for both dry and wet rot, is a 20% moisture content.

**15 Examination of joinery
drawings and
specification**

The first step for a Clerk of Works is to examine the joinery drawings, in particular, window drawings, and to study the specification.
1 If the windows, for example, are light in section, particularly the opening lights, and are set in sheer faces, without weather protection, then the Clerk of Works will know he must be relentless in his

inspections knowing that he has no latitude whatever. If the windows are stout in section with no possible torsional deformation of opening light, and a solid job set in deep reveals, then the Clerk of Works may not find his work so onerous.

2 Note whether there are any horizontal surfaces, such as top surfaces of sills or rails that might hold rainwater or condensation and could with advantage be sloped off to shed such moisture.

3 Note whether condensation channels are shown, and whether they are drained.

4 Note what capillary channels are shown, and their size and shape.

5 Examine the joint details, particularly the main frame joints for possibilities of keeping end grain to a minimum.

6 Check the window/wall joint detail—a rebate in the frame or a lap joint, as appropriate, enables sufficient width of mastic to be used. Remember one of the basic principles about mastic joints—the mastic jointing, never permanent for the life of a building, should be accessible and it should be easy of inspection, and readily replaceable.

7 Check the types of frame joints, if shown, and the types of glues specified. Brief yourself as to the correct appearance of the specified glue. Often at a glance it is possible to tell that the wrong glue is used, as so frequently happens.

16 Sample items of joinery

It will be normal for a joinery manufacturer to supply sample items of important joinery, especially windows, for approval before bulk manufacture is undertaken. The Clerk of Works should meticulously examine this sample with the Job Architect, noting any particular bad features or difficulties, so that the manufacturer has guidance on the lines on which he may proceed. This approval of sample however does not take the place of inspections and fully detailed joinery inspections of all delivered joinery must of course take place; and additionally, a random selected frame, or frames, must be subjected to breakdown examination.

17 Visits to joinery works

When bulk manufacture of windows and other joinery has commenced and a first delivery of joinery is nearly ready, the Clerk of Works, accompanied by two members of the joinery inspection team from the Sites Manager's Office, with the Job Architect if he so desires, should visit the joinery works and make a detailed inspection of the joinery which should include windows. It may be necessary to repeat visits to the joinery works until the competence of the joinery manufacturer has been fully assessed as regards the quality of his products, and he is working on the right lines; thereafter it will usually be appropriate to examine joinery as it is delivered to site.

18 Rules for visits to Works

When Clerks of Works visit joinery works, or for that matter any other works on inspection duties, the party should consist of never less than a team of two officers. They should proceed in either Council, public or their own transport, and meals or similar refreshments are to be taken under the officers' own arrangements only. Arrangements should be made, even if the joinery works is some distance away, for the visiting officers to arrive at the works early in the day, normally not later than 9 a.m., and leave only when a satisfactory day's inspection has been carried out. The Sites Manager's office will arrange transport where required, and the Site Clerk of Works should notify that office when visits to works, or site inspections of joinery, are required.

19 Guidance notes on joinery inspections

The *Joinery Inspection Report form* acts as the Clerk of Works or other inspecting officer's *Check List*. This can be obtained from the Sites Manager's Office, or from the Materials Section. A copy of this is included as an Appendix at the end of this section for reference.
As priming hides the surface, and therefore many of the imperfections, the joinery must be inspected before it is primed.
In the inspection of joinery with special reference to the items of external joinery under greatest exposure, such as windows, a literal interpretation of the specification without the balancing influence of a wide experience and a knowledge of suitability for purpose would be inadequate, but nevertheless the Clerk of Works must realise that there are restrictive limits to the quality of joinery that may be accepted by the officers of this department.
The following notes are a guide as to where emphasis is to be placed in inspections of detail:—

1 *Timber mark* should be noted whenever timber in bulk is being inspected.

2 *Species* of timber should be ascertained from the manager or buyer of the joinery firm, via the main contractor as appropriate, so that all parties concerned are fully aware of the potential weaknesses which the visiting officers will be discussing.

3 *Moisture content* is to be checked by meter in several positions and recorded.

4 *Preservative* treatment is one of our two most important safeguards for external joinery. The method used, and the method of certification, is to be noted.

5 **Joints:** first class workmanship in jointing with full glue sealing with the correct glue is our second important safeguard, and this without question must be checked by the Clerk of Works and other inspecting officers.
If crevices are present these must be filled after priming with a white lead oil paste stopping. Contrary to the impressions of some joiners, nails are not an acceptable substitute for non-ferrous dowel pins.

6 **Glued work:** It must be emphasised that glued work in joints must be efficiently carried out to be acceptable. The provisions of British Standard 1186 and of Code of Practice 153(2) page 9, must be known by every Clerk of Works in this respect.
This is one of the matters that must be given special attention in the breakdown examination by Quality-Control of a random selected frame.

7 **End grain:** This is particularly vulnerable to the ingress of moisture and should be at an absolute minimum, and fully treated by preservative, and of course later fully protected by a thoroughly well applied full bodied primer.

8 **General finish** and appearance of all joinery work should be examined and commented upon. It should be noted that British Standard 1186, part 2, ' Workmanship in Joinery ' implies that unless otherwise specified, and these are the operative words, surfaces of joinery to be painted may not be satisfactory for painting with gloss paint. This will not do for the department and such surfaces must be appropriately rubbed down.

9 **Growth rings** and their number per inch give an indication of the speed of growth, the coarseness of end grain, and the ease or otherwise of the surface machining of the timber. They are guidance figures only and only outstanding deviations from the specified figures need be noted.

10 **Slope of grain,** which must be limited to avoid possible warping, depends to some extent naturally, on its use, and experience dictates here, but normally there should be no difficulty in obtaining at most one in ten, local deviations being ignored.

11 **Splits and shakes** give any examiner some idea of the general quality of the timber and its history of variation in moisture content; splits and shakes should not be viewed complacently.
These timber faults are covered in British Standard 1186, although some consider not very strictly.

64

The Clerk of Works should not relax his insistence on strict compliance with this as a minimum standard.

12 *Pith,* i.e., the heart of the log, is not permissible, under any circumstances on exposed faces of external joinery.

13 *Blue Stain* as an unsightly discolouration should be avoided where possible. Unless dealt with in the specification it is allowed other than for clear finish work, by the latest edition, 1971, of British Standard 1186.

14 *Knots*—that are small, sound and tight are, in general, acceptable, particularly in isolation. The exact guidance knot sizes that are acceptable are specified in some detail in British Standard 1186 of 1971, but the use to which timber is put is important, and sensible considerations should invariably prevail. For example sound knots on an inside face are usually immaterial, whereas on an exposed face of the higher classifications of timber only the occasional tight small knot would be passed.

15 *Plugging* in place of knots is of course permissible in sensible locations. If a Clerk of Works is in doubt about a knot or series of knots, not in a clear finish surface he should visualise the position if a small annular hole was in place of the knot or knots concerned. If such a hole would allow water into the building, or into the internals of a joint, then plugging in such a position would not be an acceptable solution.

The contractor who produces, to meet the higher classifications of timber, a member which has a cluster or continuous line of plugs in place of a number of arris or margin knots, as has occurred, maintaining that the timber has ' no knots ' within the meaning of the specification should be told that he is wasting his time.

16 *Decay and Insect Attack* are naturally causes of rejection of the joinery component involved, and if such is found the inspection should not proceed further without reference to the architect-in-charge.

The Joinery Inspection Report form should be completed in full. The general principle is that the inspection team reporting are to supply the architect-in-charge with clear factual information and positive recommendations from which he will be able to make the necessary decisions and issue instructions for the contractor accordingly.

A copy of the report should not be given by the Clerk of Works to either main contractor, sub-contractor or supplier. The distribution should be Architect-in-Charge

(2), Sites Manager (1), Clerks of Works (1), AR/TC (1), and file (1). This is noted on the Report Form.

20 Earlier Specifications

Earlier Housing Branch specifications directed that softwood for external joinery was to be completely free of sapwood. These specifications are still in circulation. When a Clerk of Works has such a specification he should advise his Job Architect that the contractor's manager should be asked what he proposes to do to meet the specified requirements on which he has tendered. The least that should happen is that the contractor should agree to the full preservative treatment of all external joinery without cost to the Council.

21 Windows for breakdown examination

Housing Specifications will normally allow for a percentage of the windows manufactured, or other especially important joinery frames, to be subjected to random selection and breakdown examination, and the Clerk of Works should check the number so specified. Where, as in the older specifications none is specified, the Clerk of Works should ascertain from the Architect in charge what the position is to be. Quite often one such frame will be all that will be required, as long as it is fully random in selection.

Needless to say these windows to be subjected to breakdown examination are *not* sample windows such as may be put up by the joinery manufacturers before bulk manufacture is commenced, but as part of the department's quality control process, are fully random samples selected by the officers inspecting the joinery for specific breakdown examination of joints, gluing, fixings, preservation and general quality.

22 Window Test rigs

This breakdown examination of selected windows with the object of detecting the faults and weaknesses that may lead to comparatively long term deterioration is separate from the procedure for obtaining the ' immediate performance ' figures from either the department's or the manufacturers window test rigs.

It is possible that both controls may however form part of a future full quality control programme.

23 The Combed Joint

This joint is essentially a glued joint and depends entirely on the efficacy with which the gluing operation is carried out, both in workmanship and glue materials, for its efficiency and dependability.

The non-ferrous star dowel usually used is not there to take the place of the glue.

This joint has gained a bad reputation, particularly amongst maintenance officers, simply because site supervision staff during construction have allowed to pass through, in many cases, an ineffectively glued joint. The Clerk of Works must watch for this.

24 Glues

Animal glues (scotch glue or fish glue) and casein glues (made from milk) fail if subjected to continual wetting and therefore should not be allowed for external joinery.
Weather and boil-proof glues (WBP), are now usually specified by the Department and are synthetic resin glues to BS 1204. Familiar names commercially are Aerodux, Cascophen, etc.

25 Notes on priming

1 Joinery has of course to be inspected before priming takes place otherwise the timber cannot be seen. Priming therefore cannot normally take place at works unless it is practicable for the inspecting officer to visit the works.
2 When priming takes place the joinery should be at, as near as possible, the correct equilibrium moisture content and this should be checked by the Clerk of Works.
3 The Clerk of Works should take samples of the priming for examination in the Council's scientific laboratories.
4 Where there is too long a time between the initial priming and the final painting so that the initial priming, in the opinion of the Clerk of Works, has deteriorated then the work should be re-primed.
5 End grain and surfaces against brickwork or concrete should have a double coat of full bodied primer.

26 Hardwood flooring on screeds

Wooden flooring, hardwood or otherwise should not be laid until the moisture content of the screed has been checked. This is best done by a direct reading hygrometer or possibly by sample test by a solution of phenolphthalein and the Clerk of Works should ask his architect to arrange for the services of the Scientific Branch to make this check.

27 Preservation— Wooden doors to garages

There have been many cases of wooden doors to garages suffering early decay, particularly in the bottom rail, and it is advisable not to forget that these doors should also be treated with preservative in the same way as other external joinery.

28 Skirtings

Timber skirtings may often be fixed to walls that have a very high moisture content. The backs of the skirtings should have a moisture resistant coating before fixing —at least equal to a coating of full bodied primer.

29 Paint protection of putties

There have been many cases where water has entered through (cracks) or behind glazing putty. Putties should be of a non-hardening type and the painting should be overlapped on to the glass, but neatly so, in every case. In modern dwellings internal condensation on glass is often considerable and where there is back puttying the Clerk of Works should check with the job Architect whether drain-away condensation channels and/or internal chamfering-off of horizontal surfaces of frames should be required.

GREATER LONDON COUNCIL
DEPARTMENT OF ARCHITECTURE & CIVIC DESIGN
JOINERY INSPECTION REPORT

DIVISION.	SITE.
ARCHITECT.	CONTRACTOR.
C. OF WORKS.	JOINERY CONTRACTOR.
REF. AR/HO/C/SM	DATE OF INSPECTION.

1	NUMBER OF ITEMS INSPECTED AND DESCRIPTION *(i.e. Ext. or Int.)*	
	PLACE OF INSPECTION.	
2	RELEVANT SPEC^N CLAUSES.	
3	FRAMES SPEC^N FOR BREAKDOWN.	
4	TIMBER MARK.	
5	TIMBER SPECIES.	
6	MOISTURE CONTENT.	
7	PRESERVATION. (a) *Method*. (b) *Type*. (c) *Method of certification*.	
8	JOINTING. *Types and workmanship*.	
9	ADHESIVE : *Type specified*.	
	Type used.	
	Workmanship.	
10	GENERAL FINISH AND APPEARANCE.	

JOINERY INSPECTION REPORT (Continued)

11	GENERAL COMMENTS ON:- (a) Growth rings. (b) Slope of grain. (c) Splits / Shakes. (d) Sapwood. (e) Blue Stain (f) Pith (g) Decay. (h) Knots. (i) Sapwood in hardwood.	
12	PRIMING	
13	CONFORMITY TO DETAIL. (by Site Clerk of Works)	
14	METHOD OF STORAGE.	
15	AVAILABILITY FOR INSPECTION.	
16	WORKS INSPECTORATE AND GENERAL ORGANISATION.	
17	NUMBERS OF COMPONENTS RECOMMENDED AS :- (a) Acceptable. (b) Not acceptable. (c) Acceptable with stated remedial measures.	
18	GENERAL COMMENTS.	

COPIES
ARCHITECT. ——— 2
SITES MANAGER. —— 1
CLERK OF WORKS.—— 1
FILE. ————— 1

INSPECTED BY :- ....

....

DATE.　　　　for SITES MANAGER.

70

14 Mastic Asphalt Roofing

1 Information necessary to all Clerks of Works

It is necessary for every building Clerk of Works in the department:

(i) To be well informed on what is good detailing in asphalt work, and what is bad,

(ii) and, to be knowledgeable about the asphalt spreader's method of working, and be able to confidently assess what is good workmanship on a job, and what is bad.

Asphalting is a specialist trade, but it is a straightforward trade, simple and direct in technique. When the very uncomplicated asphalt operation is clearly understood, the rest, design detailing, general technique, and good workmanship, is simply basic building commonsense.

2 Definition of Mastic Asphalt

Essentially mastic asphalt is simply a mix of asphaltic cement and suitably graded aggregates, brought to the site in solid block form, melted to an appropriately molten state and spread, on a dry surface while hot, by means of hand tools, to give a dense durable skin sealing any part of a building e.g. a roof, against the entrance of water. At no time shall molten asphalt exceed 230°C.

3 BRS check on asphalt roofs

The Building Research Station undertook the survey of a number of flat roofs surfaced with mastic asphalt. It is interesting to note that one third of the total roofs examined had let water penetrate at one time or another and this is especially of interest to the Clerk of Works in that practically all the failures noted were due to neglecting to follow standard, laid down, recommendations for

1 detailing and specifying the work, or

2 workmanship in installation, in particular at edges, skirtings, kerbs, outlets and parapets.

A similar examination of asphalted roofs in this department, in 1972 and early 1973, but carried out on an ' as required ' basis, revealed very much the same pattern of fault, and for the same reasons.

4 Successful use of Mastic Asphalt

Assuming uniformly good quality asphalt material, the successful use of mastic asphalt depends upon:

1 The base on which the asphalt is to be laid, which must be stable, with the surface flush, and without gaps of any kinds.

2 The adequacy of the detailing, e.g. skirtings, kerbs, outlets, tuck-ins, flashings etc.

3 Good workmanship.

4 Protection of finished asphalt work both in new building operations or in alteration work.

5 Appropriate inspections by Clerk of Works

The Clerk of Works must not leave this specialist work entirely to the specialist, without inspecting it as efficiently as he does the other major building trades; and the senior Clerk of Works on the site must remember that although this is work on roofs, and perhaps because of that, there is no substitute whatsoever for his going up and giving the work a close examination personally.

6 Typical faults

Typical faults that have occurred, are as follows, given approximately in order of frequency of occurrence:

	Fault	Remedy
1	Slipshod workmanship in fixing of woodwool slabs in preparation of base—slabs uneven, corners broken, excessive gaps, insufficient nailing, joints not taped, free standing kerbs not detailed.	Better site supervision, and more precise detailing.
2	Crazing of asphalt surface.	Not of the utmost gravity; should have been obviated by site supervision insistence on adequate sand rubbing.
3	Skirtings under thickness.	Check by site supervision having samples cut out for checking on site.
4	Trapped moisture in screeds.	Use screed with minimum water content; completely protect against water until sealed by asphalting.
5	Asphalt failure at expansion joints.	Better detailing at expansion joint.
6	Serious cracks in asphalt at internal angle fillet.	Detailing; free standing kerbs, or similar preventive detail.
7	Inadequate chase for tuck-ins.	Site supervision of chase cutting.
8	Slipshod workmanship round cradle bolts or similar.	Site supervision of metal priming in advance; site supervision of detail work.
9	Slumping of asphalt turn ups.	Check adequate keying to surface; also have composition of asphalt subjected to analysis—this may be faulty.
10	Incorrect fixing of flashing, and trim.	Site supervision; firm fixing and allowance for expansion.

| 11 | Warping of timber deck on which asphalt is to be laid | Site supervision must insist that boarding is protected; not exposed to weather for any length of time (asphalt must be spread on felt underlay). |

7 Reflective treatments

Where felspar chippings on hot bitumen dressing compound are not specified, then a suitable reflective paint could well be used, and it could be helpful if the Clerk of Works check with the architect-in-charge whether such roof paint could be used to provide an appropriate finish to the job. The Director of Housing does not favour the use of chippings.

8 A small working gang, and its tools and equipment

A small gang could consist of, typically:
Spreader charge hand
Second spreader
Potman, labourer
Tipper, labourer.

Tools:
Floats (including rounded coving floats and sharp round gutter float)
Filleters (with wooden nidgers to get into corners)
Spatulas (for vertical or near vertical application)
Skirting trowels
Cold chisel
Boasting chisel
Handsaw
Hammer
Metal cutters
Underlay cutting knife.

Equipment:
Knee-pads
Straight edge
Spirit level
Gauges (wooden prepared thicknessing battens)
Chalk line and chalk
Steel tape.

Plant:
Mechanical mixer boiler, or
Portable asphalt pot (for small jobs)
Hand roller
Sieves
Hand brooms and brushes
Buckets.

Materials:
Blocks of asphalt (kite marked)

Sand
Underlay felt
Metal lathing
Chippings (as required)
Reflective paint
Aluminium edging
Bitumen dressing compound (as required)
Metal primer.

9 Typical working operations

The base on which the asphalt is to be laid is checked and any necessary preparatory work completed.

1 The mastic asphalt blocks are broken up and melted in the pot or mixer-boiler.

2 The surface on which the asphalt is to be applied is brushed clean and dry, underfelt is laid, gauges are set out about 2 metres apart, of same thickness as the asphalt to be spread.

3 The melted asphalt is brought by bucket (dusted), tipped at the working position keeping the working edge hot, and spread evenly by hand float, achieving an even surface when the initial spreading is completed, by repeated sweeps of the float. New supplies of melted asphalt are spread slightly over the edge of the previous one to keep it soft, and the join is welded together by float. This overlap joint welded by float and temporary application of hot material enables join to be formed. Blows are pierced and made good while asphalt is warm.

4 On further coats the joins are staggered; 150mm for horizontal work and 75mm in vertical work would be appropriate. All joins must be clean and free from sand or dust.

5 Graded sand is then rubbed by float (and not just brushed) into the top surface, unless some other definite treatment is specified. This sand-rubbing gives a matt surface, removes the thin skin of rich bitumen, akin to 'laitance' in concrete work, and restrains the development of the crazing which disfigures quite a number of asphalt surfaces.

6 On important roofs white spar, or similar, chippings, in bitumen dressing compound, well rolled by hand roller, can be laid to prevent excessive heat transmission through the asphalt membrane, or if this is not done to dress with reflective paint.

10 The underlay

Buildings, sub-structures, bases, all move in some degree. The use of an ' isolating membrane ', or underlay usually of black sheathing felt, is to make sure that the building movement has no effect whatever on the continuity and water-tightness of the asphalt skin. The Clerk of Works will see that this is just common sense.

He will also see that where vertical or sloping work is involved, when an underlay is necessary, as it is in the case of a timber surface, steps must be taken to fasten the underlay in position; and this is done, on the timber, by clout headed felt nails at 150 mm intervals, ready to receive metal lathing similarly nailed. The Clerk of Works should note that an underlay is not necessary on vertical or steeply sloping concrete or similar surfaces. Timber is a special case as being subject to movement.

Bitumen sheathing felt underlays avoid ceiling staining which can be caused by leaching of bitumen from black felt type of underlay.

11 Overall thickness of asphalt and number of coats

When the total asphalt thickness required has been determined by experience of the particular use involved, the number of coats or applications within that thickness depends upon the maximum thickness a good spreader can apply on the various surfaces in flat, sloping, and vertical positions.

Where asphalt is laid on steep or vertical surfaces, the first coat should be regarded as for adhesive purposes only, and to form an adequate base for the normal applications. Usually for roofing work, with which this section of the Handbook is concerned, two coats, additional to the special adhesive coat, are appropriate.

12 Temporary applications of asphalt

It is of interest to note that the asphalt trade is unusual inasmuch as purely temporary applications of the main material, molten asphalt, are used quite considerably usually simply for heating purposes.

1 When mastic asphalt is to be removed hot molten mastic asphalt is placed upon it and when the required area is sufficiently hot the mastic over coat is removed and the existing asphalt is cut out.

2 Where the edge of a mastic asphalt layer is contaminated it is cleaned by a temporary application of hot molten asphalt.

3 When asphalt is being joined to asphalt hot molten asphalt is taken over the edge of the older asphalt, and left long enough to enable the join to be welded by float.

4 When solid internal fillets are being formed, adequate heat, and cleanliness, are essential. After the necessary thorough cleaning with a brush, hot molten asphalt is applied to a length of the intersection, and after a short time is removed. The warmed and softened intersection, after being worked with a filleter, to clean and remove a thin layer of the flat asphalt, then has fresh asphalt applied, and formed into the required solid fillet (two coats).

13 Detailing

Where no specific detail is shown on drawings; or if required for comparison purposes with details shown, a range of reliable details are shown in Figures 1-19 of Code of Practice 144, part 4, 1970, a copy of which should be in the possession of every building Clerk of Works; with however the query on details 1 and 2 as mentioned below. The list of details are as follows for ready reference:

1 Skirting to brick wall, screeded roof.
2 Skirting to concrete wall, screeded roof.
3 Skirting and dpc to wall, screeded roof.
4 Skirting on free-standing kerb, timber roof.
5 Tiled finish, screeded finish.
6 Skirting and dpc to wall, insulation boarding.
7 Eaves finish gutter flashing.
8 Drip apron to roof verge.
9 Verge finish with edge trim.
10 Concrete kerb finish, wood sill over.
11 Finish to metal sill.
12 Lining to roof reservoir.
13 Finish to kerb as water check.
14 Rainwater outlet through parapet.
15 Flat roof twin kerb expansion joint.
16 Sleeve outlet.
17 Cast iron outlet.
18 Cast iron pipe through concrete roof.
19 Finish round metal standards.

14 Improvements to certain details

Experience in the department does throw some doubt on the long term efficacy of the details 1 and 2 of the tuck-in method of skirting finish to brick walls and concrete walls.

The composition of the asphalt, the shaping of the tuck-in groove, the efficiency or otherwise of the flashing or pointing hold-fasts, or, more probably, the ineffectiveness of the keying to brick or concrete vertical face, may have contributed to the partial failures that have been experienced.

This however is being subjected to further research, and the Clerk of Works could well contribute to this by very careful examination, over as lengthy a period as possible, of the detail concerned, and having a discussion about the detail as used on his contract with the specialist Technical Officer in asphalt work, of the Site Managers Group.

15 Plastering

1 Trueness of the plastering system

Clause 37 of BS 5492, 1977—Internal Plastering— reads as follows:
Two coats of plaster can correct only minor irregularities in the background or small deviation from line or plumb.
Provided, however, that the surface to be plastered is brought to a fair line, and the ground and linings are fixed to a true and plumb line, then the application of a plaster of the order of 13 mm thick to solid backgrounds, other than concrete, can be expected to produce a reasonably smooth and flat surface within the following tolerances, i.e. the plaster should not show any deviation of more than 3 mm from a 1800 mm straight edge placed against it. Plumbness can be achieved only with three-coat work, excluding dubbing, with a thickness of the order of 19 mm.
No tolerance can be laid down for plastering of less than 13 mm nominal thickness since this will closely follow the contour of the background, but with a sufficiently true surface of plasterboard or concrete a similar tolerance may be obtainable.
The tolerance for three-coat work on a solid background should not be inferior to that for two-coat work.'

2 Thin coat

The British Standard lays down no tolerance for a thin coat, i.e., coat less than 13 mm thick because this coat will closely follow the contour of the background. The code considers that a similar tolerance to that quoted should be obtained on a sufficiently true surface of plasterboard or concrete.

3 1 in 600 tolerance

While this information, i.e., a general surface tolerance of 1 in 600, (3 mm from a 1800 mm straight edge) is a guide, it should be noted that this in itself does not provide a completely satisfactory method of specifying work since many walls which would comply with this would not be acceptable in practice. Nevertheless the stipulation of not more than 3 mm deviation over a length of 1800 mm is in fact a guide to the standard of surface workmanship that one can have reason for expecting.

4 Quality of workmanship in plastering

Quality of the workmanship is most important in plastering work, and the skill of the operatives employed. The Clerk of Works must be particularly vigilant in inspecting the first piece of fully finished work that is done—this should be inspected with more than usual care—and endeavour should be made to impress upon the contractor the standard of quality required.
On no account may the contractor be permitted, in default of the Clerk of Works immediate inspection of the first finished work, to carry on with work below standard;

nor is it any extenuation that irregularity in surface is sometimes difficult to detect until decoration is applied.

5	**Sample dwellings**	The Clerk of Works should make it a rule that on each contract, by arrangement with the architect-in-charge and with the contractor, the first dwelling should be prepared as a sample dwelling, first showing the quality of the plastering work required by the department and then taken to the final decorating stage to show the standard of quality required by the department in finishes generally. This sample dwelling may also show plumbing layout if desired.
6	**Preparation of background for plastering**	The Clerk of Works should see that the background is properly prepared before plastering work is commenced and in particular that brickwork joints are properly raked out and concrete properly hacked for effective key. Concrete surfaces that are to be plastered should be roughened by hacking as soon as possible after shuttering is removed, unless spatterdash or similar methods are specified. Where dubbing out is required the Clerk of Works is to see that sufficient time is given before the application of the first plastering coat to enable the dubbing material to fully dry out.
7	**Excessive making good of plaster**	The need for excessive making good is usually the sign of badly organised work and seriously mars the overall quality of finish. The Clerk of Works in the interest of good finish should pursue the constant aim of keeping the necessary making good to an absolute minimum.
8	**Cleanliness in plastering**	Cleanliness is essential in carrying out good plaster work and the Clerk of Works is to see that adequate protection is given to finished work, including concrete sub-floors where set droppings of plaster, unless completely removed, will cause lifting of floor screeds. The Clerk of Works is to ensure that where sanitary ware is fixed before plastering is commenced, it is protected by board cover or similar means. The Clerk of Works must not permit droppings in baths, basins or sinks. The Clerk of Works is also to see that CCUs are covered and protected during plastering work.
9	**Mixes for plastering**	The Clerk of Works should see that the plastering materials and plastering mix are correct to the specification and that in the case of special proprietary materials the agreed recommendations and special instructions of the manufacturers are followed.
10	**Detailed inspection of plaster work**	When inspecting plaster work the Clerk of Works should particularly examine walls at ceiling line, walls at skirting

line, internal angles and the maintenance of width at reveals and returns. External angles are always fairly obvious. General surfaces may need to be examined against a side light and with a straight rule, surface roughness being checked by sweeping hand across the surface.

11 Sound insulating quilt

Where an insulating quilt of glass or rockwool is laid it is the Clerk of Works responsibility to see that it is turned up at all edges, that it is completely continuous under the screed and that no direct bond or contact whatsoever is permitted between the screed and the structural floor or the walls, either around the edges or between the length of quilt. A few square inches of such direct contact will affect the insulation value of the whole floor. It is the Clerk of Works responsibility to see by careful supervision that this does not occur.

12 Screed for thermoplastic tiles

The Clerk of Works is to obtain an assurance for each floor of the block from the thermoplastic tile sub-contractor, before the latter commences laying that the screed is perfectly acceptable. This assurance should be recorded in the Clerk of Works diary.
Regardless of this assurance of acceptability the Clerk of Works is in addition to assure himself personally that the screed is true and level, free of imperfections and to the standard required by the department, including, and this is important, being to the required thickness.

13 Protection from weather

During the plastering operation there must be adequate protection from the weather. This usually means that the building should be glazed before the plastering is commenced. If not other protective measures must be taken and the Clerk of Works should see that this is done.

14 Temporary lighting

Plasterers cannot do good work in poor light. Where natural lighting is insufficient the Clerk of Works is to see that adequate temporary electric lighting is provided.

15 Patching

It is good practice to see that the area of work left for subsequent ' patching ' is kept to the absolute minimum.

16 Bonding agents

Considerable attention should be paid by the Clerk of Works to obtaining an adequate key for plasterwork particularly base rendering work. For particularly important work full hacking is usually specified and contractors sometimes ask whether a bonding ' agent ' added to the mix may be used in place of the key. The Clerk of Works should strongly advise his Job Architect against this.

The use of an additive bonding agent makes supervision difficult, as unless a Clerk of Works is with the plasterers all the time he cannot be certain that the correct bonding agent is used, or in fact that a bonding agent is used at all. *If* a bonding agent is specified the precise agent approved and used should be known to the Clerk of Works and he should see that he has details as to correct method of use from the manufacturers and particularly of the preliminary cleaning of surface to be rendered

17 Preference for mechanical key

On important work, keying to a concrete surface by full and proper hacking removes laitance and is far and away the better method and what is more the Clerk of Works can very rapidly check at any time whether the work of hacking has been carried out and whether it has been done properly.

16 Decoration

1 Inspection—general

The Clerk of Works is to ensure that:
1 The surfaces to be painted are adequately prepared and are perfectly dry.
2 The types and brands of paints applied are completely in accordance with the specification and are approved for use *before* painting is commenced.
3 The correct number of coats are applied.
4 The standard of skill and workmanship, of cleanliness, and of general finished appearance are entirely satisfactory.
The Clerk of Works is not to permit the contractor to commence painting on a surface, or any piece of work, which is not completely ready, in all respects.

2 Quality of finished work

The chief points on which the general quality of the decorative work can be judged by visual inspection are the following, and the Clerk of Works in his inspections is to take account of all these points:
1 Uniformity of finish and colour.
2 Uniform and complete obscuration of the ground.
3 Freedom from any blemishes, such as runs, sags, wrinklings, fat edges and starved patches.
4 Freedom from tackiness.
5 Freedom from conspicuous brush marks or ' ladders '.
6 General cleanliness, neatness of line, and no disfigurement of neighbouring surfaces.

3 Preparation

Correct preparation of surfaces is all-important both before the first coat is applied, and between coats, and the Clerk of Works is to see that the provisions of the specification in this respect are followed in detail. Work must not be covered by paint if this preparation has been inadequately carried out, and the Clerk of Works must not permit painting to proceed under these circumstances.

4 Dry surfaces

In general, climatic conditions before, during and after painting have a most marked effect on the immediate success of the work, and on the subsequent life of the paint. In particular moisture is a potent danger to successful decoration. For this reason the Clerk of Works is to make sure that the building has sufficiently dried out and the surfaces to be painted are free from dampness before decoration is applied. The Clerk of Works should not permit decoration to be applied under very damp air conditions at the position of the work, and in particular spraying should not be permitted during or immediately after rain.
The Clerk of Works is to ensure that adequate ventilation to rooms is maintained in warm weather.

5	**Faulty materials**	If in spite of tests of materials, and the use of an approved paint, during the course of the work the paint itself appears to be faulty, in colour, consistency, drying time, or quality of finish, the Clerk of Works should instruct the contractor to cease that part of the work, and inform the architect-in-charge, who will call in the paint manufacturer, and the department's Paint Inspector.
6	**Number of coats of paint**	Successive undercoats should show a gradation in colour leading up to that of the finish, and so that the Clerk of Works can readily check the number of coats applied, he should insist that the variation of shade is sufficiently distinctive to allow such check to be made without difficulty.
7	**Cleanliness of finished paint work**	Apart from the requirement of general cleanliness during working, and at the completion of decoration, the Clerk of Works is not to permit soiling of the decorations through later work by other trades, for example electricians, plumbers, and floor layers. If any serious soiling does occur the Clerk of Works must see that the marks are completely removed, and that the finish coat is re-applied on the whole of the wall area of the surface concerned.
8	**Delivery of paint**	Only paints delivered in decorated cans, or with the standard printed label affixed bearing the approved brand name, are to be accepted on site; neither type-written labels nor composite labels are to be accepted. Paints delivered in any other way are to be rejected by the Clerk of Works, who should report accordingly to the architect-in-charge, as well as noting the rejection in his weekly report and diary. Cans must all bear a batch number.
9	**Dilution of paints— general**	The policy is that paints are to be used exactly as received from the makers in accordance with the maker's instructions and the addition of thinners, driers, or other material will only be permitted when specifically *required* by the makers, and the procedure approved by the architect-in-charge. All Clerks of Works are to work within the terms of this instruction. If the paints as received from the makers are not completely suitable for use then the contractor must see that these are removed from the site and are replaced by paints which are suitable for use as received.
10	**Primers for joinery**	Priming paints are a case in point where in far too many instances sampling tests have shown that there has been heavy thinning in the paint kettles. The excuse

usually made has been that the priming paint is too thick.

In fact primers are at times produced that do appear somewhat thick, and in cold conditions may offer some genuine difficulty in application. This may be due to insufficient stirring when the can is first opened, too lengthy storage, storage in bad conditions, or possibly incorrect formulation by the makers. If the thickness is due to insufficient stirring another can newly opened and adequately stirred immediately offers the appropriate solution. In every other case the correct attitude, and answer, of the Clerk of Works, is that the manufacturer must supply to the site correctly constituted primers that are suitable for use direct from the can, in place of the too thick material, and that if priming work is to proceed on the site this must be done immediately.

11   Brushes for priming joinery

Very often the priming of joinery on site is regarded as an unimportant chore, by the agent, that can be carried out by any available labourer, using worn out or discarded brushes or ' scrubs '. The importance of the protective value of good priming is such that this attitude must be corrected by the Clerk of Works.

Priming should be applied, on site, by a skilled operative. A brush should be used, as the friction of the brush helps to displace air and to ensure that the paint makes maximum contact with the surface.

A metal bound and cemented brush is preferable, made from black bristles, sufficiently stiff to carry heavy paints. A three inch brush might be appropriate for large areas but nothing larger than a two inch brush should be used for door and window frames.

12   Paint tests

The Clerk of Works is to arrange for tests of paints, from suppliers cans, and from kettles, early in the contract and thereafter as may be found advisable or as instructed by the architect-in-charge.

Priming paint is to be tested, and if priming already applied is suspect scrapings can be tested under instructions from the architect-in-charge.

Details of the Clerk of Works duties in connection with sampling and the forwarding of samples to the Scientific Adviser's paint section are given in the chapter of these instructions entitled ' TESTING '. Every batch should be tested, the different batches being identified by the batch number on the bottom of the suppliers' cans.

13   Paint sampling

Routine paint sampling for test is the responsibility of the Clerk of Works and the Clerk of Works must not expect that this may be left to the department's Paint Inspector, whose duty is advisory.

When taking a sample for laboratory examination it is essential to stir the paint thoroughly and to practically fill the sample tin. The lid of the tin should be replaced without delay and the tin shaken.

Standard labels are available and on these all the information required (including the brand name in full detail) should be entered. Samples of both undercoat and finish should be submitted. Should a sample be found unsatisfactory on laboratory examination, it will normally be required that an unopened can be submitted for checking purposes.

14 Excessive thinning of paints

As various reports and summaries of paint testing over the last few years have shown the main irregularity revealed in sampling from painters kettles on site is often excessive thinning. This thinning, of course, is usually by liquids of low specific gravity, e.g., the use of water excessively in the thinning of emulsion paints. When such thinning occurs the density of the thinned mixture is lower than it should be for correct use. Therefore by comparing the weights of equal volumes of the paint from the kettles with that direct from the makers previously unopened cans the thinning can be readily detected and the percentage dilution assessed.

15 'Instant paint testing'

Hence by the aid of disposable plastic containers, each holding an equal volume of paint, and a pair of simple scales, dilution can be detected and assessed immediately on the site and in fact, if necessary, at the point of test sampling. Where excessive thinning is revealed in this manner, the Clerk of Works can take the necessary action immediately and there is no need to wait for the several days while paint samples are sent back to the County Hall laboratories for test.

Instructions and training, and the provision of the necessary apparatus can be arranged either direct by the Sites Managers Group of the Housing Branch, or through the Materials Information Group.

16 List of approved brands

The department maintains a list of approved brands of paints, each identified by its particular brand name. This is a restricted document and is regularly reviewed. When a contractor submits brand names of the paints he proposes to use, these are checked against the department's approved list and the architect-in-charge informs the Clerk of Works of the brands that have been so approved. No other brands of paint may be used on the contract unless special approval in advance for this variation of brands is given.

17 Protection of Finished Work and Protection in Storage

1 General protection

All work completed or partly completed on site, and all building materials or components brought on site by the contractor for incorporation in the work are thereafter the property of the Council. As such the Clerk of Works is to see that they have the protection required for Council property. Protection of finished work including finished concrete work carried out early in the contract either by the main contractor or a sub-contractor, must have the Clerk of Works' constant attention and he must see that the main contractor provides or arranges for efficient protection of such work.

2 Orderliness of site

The Clerk of Works is to see that the site is kept in an orderly condition, and the contractor should be discouraged from untidy methods of working and untidy distribution of materials. In particular debris and waste from one trade is often permitted to hinder the work of a following trade; this is usually due to ineffective supervision by the contractor's staff. The Clerk of Works should, as far as it is practicable, see that the debris of one trade is removed before the following trade commences operations.

3 Waste of materials

The Clerk of Works should see that there is no undue waste of materials on site. If undue waste is taking place and continues after the contractor has been warned, the Clerk of Works should report accordingly to the architect-in-charge so that the matter may be dealt with at a site meeting, and properly recorded and minuted.

4 Stonework and Precast work

The Clerk of Works is to see that all stonework and precast work brought on to the site is stored in a place where it is not liable to damage, that until it is built in, it is properly protected, and that after being built in all edges and surfaces are properly cased up for adequate protection as early as practicable.

5 Protection of new brickwork

The Clerk of Works is to see that no material is stacked, even temporarily, against the external walls of the building, and that no water from uncompleted down pipes or other sources is allowed to discharge against the finished work.

The tops of the wall in newly erected brickwork should be covered during rain to prevent mortar being washed out of the joints; scaffold boards are adequate for this or other form of cover such as tarpaulin or sacking. The inner board of any working scaffold should be turned up during rain to prevent splashing and staining of the brick face. The Clerk of Works should see that these precautions are observed as a regular normal routine.

6	**Protective measures for concrete**	The Clerk of Works is to see that newly placed concrete is adequately protected against drying winds, sun, heavy rain and frost, and is not subjected to loads, shocks, vibration or traffic of any kind until it is properly matured and he should see that the provisions of the specification are strictly observed in these respects. The surfaces and arrises of finished concrete work must be efficiently protected against staining or damage.
7	**Protection in storage**	The contractor is responsible under the contract for ensuring the proper storage and handling of articles supplied under the Council's bulk purchase arrangements; and the Clerk of Works is to make quite sure that proper handling, storage and protection, is given to such articles. It is also necessary that the materials and articles supplied by the contractor for use in the work are properly handled and given the storage and protection adequate to the material or article in question. The Clerk of Works should make the contract requirements in this respect perfectly clear to the contractor. If after warning, a contractor continues to neglect his responsibilities in these respects, or if he has insufficient storage sheds or covers on site, the Clerk of Works should report such neglect to the architect-in-charge to be dealt with at site meeting.
8	**Storage of sanitary goods**	Sanitary goods must be stored under cover, and the Clerk of Works must never permit these goods, including baths, to remain in the open exposed to the weather. In the case of baths these should normally be stacked vertically tap-hole end downwards, supported on wood battens, and packed at all enamel points of contact.
9	**Plumbing—Frost precautions**	Where flats are completed but not yet handed over and very frosty weather occurs the Clerk of Works is to ensure that the plumbing system is drained until frost danger is over.
10	**Storage of metal windows**	The Clerk of Works is to ensure that metal windows are properly stacked on edge on wooden battens, with the opening sections closed and secured. They should not be stacked on ashes or cinders.
11	**Handling of baths**	The British Bath Manufacturers' Association of Fleming House, Renfrew Street, Glasgow G3 6TG, issue a pamphlet on ' How to Handle Baths ' and British Standard 1189—Cast Iron Baths, gives good recommendations for care of baths.
12	**General storage and stacking of baths**	Baths should be kept under cover, stacked and rested vertically with tap-hole ends supported on wooden

battens, each bath separated from the next by dust sheets or polythene sheet.

Try to have the baths delivered as near as may be possible to the time they are installed, keep them dry and do not pack them in straw.

A bath can be slid into its recess by moving it on two slightly greased metal slips.

The client, the Director of Housing, will not accept baths which have been damaged and have been faked up in any way, as is mentioned in the section of this handbook entitled ' MATERIALS. '

Inspection is to be carried out in a most thorough manner.

3 Record in duplicate all defects noted at this inspection retaining one copy and handing one copy to the Contractor's agent or foreman with the instruction that all defects or omissions noted are to be remedied before the date of handover.

4 If it becomes apparent that the contractor will not have remedied all the defects listed at the Preliminary Inspection by the date projected for the Final Handover, then the Clerk of Works is to advise the architect-in-charge immediately by telephone and request that arrangements be made to postpone the date of the Final Handover. It is to be emphasised that the Clerk of Works should on no account advise the architect-in-charge that the work is ready for Final Handover until the Clerk of Works has personally ascertained that all the defects listed at the Preliminary Inspection are remedied.

6 Formal Handing-over Inspection

At the appointed date of handover a formal inspection will be made by the architect-in-charge, and the Area Surveyor, or other appropriate officer, with the Clerk of Works in attendance.

The Clerk of Works is to list in triplicate, using a pen or ball-point, any defects or omissions which are noted as still remaining. The lists will be signed by the officer taking over the building and by the Clerk of Works. One copy will be handed to the contractor's agent immediately, one copy forwarded to the architect-in-charge, and one copy retained by the Clerk of Works. Clearance of defects in lift installations to be certified by lift inspector before hand over of dwellings.

7 Formal notification to Contractor of Defects from Formal Handing over Inspection

The architect-in-charge will arrange that copies of the defects list are distributed to all departments concerned, and that a formal notification is made to the Contractor, together with a list of the defects that all such defects are to be remedied within seven days from the date of the formal inspection. The Clerk of Works will receive a copy of this letter and will check that the work is done.

8 Dilatoriness in Remedying Defects

Contractors are very often dilatory in remedying defects, sometimes due to not having an efficient ' snagging ' foreman and an effective methodical ' snagging ' procedure, sometimes due to having insufficient of the right sort of men on the work.

The Clerk of Works must arrange to maintain quiet pressure on the Contractor until all ' snags ' right through the procedure including the final defects noted at the Formal Handing Over Inspection, are fully completed.

18 Completed Buildings— Handing Over

1 Use of permanent lifts

To assist progress and supervision in tall blocks nearing the completion stage, where to facilitate construction the temporary passenger hoists provided by the contractor have had to be dismantled, the permanent lifts will be made available subject to certain specific conditions.

The Clerk of Works should note that the lifts may be made available some two months prior to the proposed date of block handover, but that before this period starts the lifts must be tested and certified by the Lift Engineer as fit for service. This certification will not be given until all builders work in connection with the lifts is completed, and the defects, or snags, in that particular work are fully remedied.

2 Use of electrical wiring

At the completion stage when snagging is being carried out internally to dwellings it is of great assistance to be able to insert bulbs in the dwellings lighting points and use the house lighting system to aid remedial snagging and inspection, particularly in the dark winter afternoons. It may be possible to obtain clearance for this to be done, and the Clerk of Works should ask the architect-in-charge; it is the practical thing to do.

3 Minimum Defects at Final Handover

It is essential that the defects or omissions at the formal handing-over to the Area Surveyor, or other appropriate receiving officer, are reduced to the absolute minimum, and the Clerk of Works bears a considerable measure of responsibility for this.

In order to achieve a smooth transfer with the minimum of difficulty to all concerned the Clerk of Works is to observe strictly the procedure that is outlined below.

4 Systematic clearance of Defects

Regular detailed inspections and checks by the Clerk of Works, with verbal instructions to the Contractor, will be made near the projected date of handover to ensure that the rectification of omissions or defects is systematically tackled by the Contractor, and that there are no major snags ahead.

5 Preliminary official Inspection

(This procedure applies to Divisions of the Housing Branch. Other Divisions will issue detailed divisional instructions as to the procedure they will adopt, or failing such instruction the Clerk of Works may use the Housing Branch procedure as a guide.)

Approximately two weeks before the day on which a building is to be handed over the Clerk of Works is to:

1 Inform the architect-in-charge of the proposed date of handover.

2 Carry out a preliminary official detailed inspection with the contractor's agent or foreman. This Preliminary

9 Troublesome 'Snagging' Lists

Sometimes it may be found that try as one may there are still a few troublesome items, stretching back into the Preliminary Official Inspection list that still have not been done at the time of the Formal Handing-Over Inspection. There is nothing else for it except to ensure that these are written in to the final defects list of the Formal Handing-Over Inspection. If this is not done these defects are liable to slip completely through the inspection net, with consequent difficulty later.

10 Timely steps, and pressure, to clear up the final few defects

As well as these minor difficulties, once the Formal Handing-Over Inspection has taken place tension is very often completely relaxed, the remedial workmen disappear, and it is very difficult indeed to get the final small defects cleared up. There is nothing so annoying as this to either clients or tenants, and the Clerk of Works must take energetic and timely steps to see that this sort of thing does not happen invoking the immediate assistance of the architect-in-charge if he cannot handle the matter himself.

11 Clerk of Works clearance certificate

As soon as in fact the Contractor has remedied all defects the Clerk of Works is to forward a certificate to that effect to the architect-in-charge. No certificate of practical completion should be issued until either the Clerk of Works clearance certificate is received, or the architect-in-charge has specifically noted and in full knowledge excluded the remaining defects.

12 Report on Completions

The successful completion and handover of dwellings is to be reported by the Clerk of Works (personally by telephone to the Sites Manager in the case of the Housing Branch) on the day of the handover, and the number of defects listed is to be given.

13 Transformer Chambers

It is essential that the Clerk of Works carries out an inspection of transformer chambers or substations at completion, similar to that of dwellings, before handing over to LEB for occupation. No handover to LEB is permitted until defects have been noted and the usual defects list made out. The usual inspection must also be made by the Clerk of Works at the end of the maintenance period.

14 Maintenance Surveys

At the end of the maintenance period defined in the contract, usually six months, a maintenance Survey is made by the architect-in-charge accompanied by the Clerk of Works and (in the Housing Branch) in co-operation with a representative of the Director of Housing. The Clerk of Works concerned will normally be the Clerk of Works in charge of the original contract.

At the Survey the Clerk of Works is to make a list on the spot of the items agreed by the architect-in-charge and the representative of the Director of Housing as being the responsibility of the Contractor. He is to hand the original to the architect-in-charge, a copy to the Contractor, a copy to the representative of the Director of Housing, and is to retain the final copy.

When the Contractor has remedied all the defects, within the terms of his contract the Clerk of Works is to certify accordingly to the architect-in-charge. It should be noted that no final certificate will be issued to the Contractor until the certificate from the Clerk of Works has been received to the effect that all maintenance defects have been remedied.

15 Recovery of Council Fencing Materials

It is the Clerk of Works duty to ensure that where a site is enclosed by fencing which is the property of the Council, such fencing is not lost to the Council at the end of the contract, or, if the Contractor refences with his own materials, at the beginning of the contract. Clerks of Works are therefore to inform the local Area Officer of the Director of Housing as soon as any Council fencing material is dismantled and ready for collection on completion of the contract or any part of the contract.

16 Horizontal Centre Pivot Windows

It is of the utmost importance that the back flap hinges to the Horizontal Centre Pivot windows should move freely throughout the whole circle of their movement. Clerks of Works should examine each of the windows with special care for any sign of binding or tightness in the knuckle. Any such tendency must be eliminated entirely before work is handed over to the Director of Housing or other authority.

17 Stopcocks

All stopcocks within dwellings should be readily accessible by doors which can easily be opened ; a screwed duct panel access is inadequate. The Clerk of Works should draw the attention of the architect-in-charge to any stopcock-access that does not conform.

18 Testing of Gas Installation

The Director of Housing will not accept handover of any dwellings unless the gas installation has been tested by the Gas Board, and a satisfactory report of such a test obtained from the Board by the main contractor. This test report is to be forwarded through the architect-in-charge to the Director of Housing.

19 Cradling Eye Bolts

1 PROVISION
All blocks of six storeys or over must be provided with bolts for the erection of cradling gear for the purpose of

repainting. Blocks under six storeys in height must also be provided with bolts where it is not possible to lean ladders against the facade for the purpose of repainting. Details of the standard cradling bolt, which is to be a direct supply item, are given on Departmental Standard Drawings Nos. D.5062 and D.5326.

2 TESTING

Cradling bolts are to be tested after fixing and before the roof finishings are laid, and for this purpose, Supplies Department has arranged for a firm to carry out the testing under a special direct payment contract. As each block becomes available for test a requisition stating the number of bolts to be tested should be issued via the Direct Supply Clerk giving at least two weeks notice of the work required.

The test certificate should be forwarded to the architect in charge for transmission to the Housing Department at handover of the block.

Note that out of a sample of 3,656 eye bolts tested 3,619 were satisfactory, and 37 failed, all failures associated with the builders' work in embedding the eyebolts.

The testing rig in use for the in-situ testing of eyebolts is operated hydraulically, and electronically records the tensile load applied to the bolt under test.

19 Sub-Contractors

1 Instructions to Sub-contractors

Any official directions on sub-contractor's work should be given to the main contractor, as a normal routine, in written form. The main contractor will then instruct his sub-contractor accordingly. Where it is on exceptional occasion expedient that the Clerk of Works verbally directs a sub-contractor it is important that the main contractor be immediately informed of such verbal direction, so that the correct channel of liability is maintained.

2 Approval of Sub-contractors

A main contractor is not permitted to let work to a sub-contractor without the prior approval of the Department. The Clerk of Works should notify the architect-in-charge where there is any case in which a sub-contractor is employed without such prior approval.

3 Nominated Sub-contractors

When a sub-contractor is selected or nominated by the Council and accepted by the main contractor who thereupon places his order with the sub-contractor, the latter for all practical purposes immediately becomes a sub-contractor of the main contractor in the normal sense, and is in every way to be treated as such by the Clerk of Works: except that under the contract there are certain obligations on the Council with regard to progress of nominated sub-contract works.

4 Direct Contractors

In certain cases the Council may enter into a direct contract covering either supply and erection, or design, supply and erection. The responsibility in this case is directly with the Council, and the Clerk of Works is to take very particular care that the work is carried out properly, and to time, fully meeting the co-ordinated programme of work for the main contract. If there is any failing in this respect the Clerk of Works should immediately inform the architect-in-charge, and also note the matter in the Weekly Report.
Where drawings are required from a direct contractor the Clerk of Works must check that such drawings are made available on site in good and sufficient time. If there is any delay whatsoever in the receipt of such drawings the Clerk of Works is to inform the architect-in-charge as well as noting the matter in the Weekly Report.

5 Direct Supplies

The Council may enter into a direct contract for the supply of certain materials, for example facing bricks, reinforcement in special cases of shortage, or any materials under the Bulk Purchase (Direct Supply) Scheme.
The responsibility for supply is directly with the Council and the Clerk of Works is to take great care to ensure

that the supply is maintained adequately to the requirements of the main contract. In the circumstances of the main contract being delayed the Clerk of Works is to make the necessary notifications and take the necessary steps generally to ensure that materials from direct supplies are not delivered too far in advance of the contractor's actual requirements.

6 Work by Outside Authorities

Work will usually be done on a contract by such outside authorities as the Gas Board, Electricity Board and G.P.O. for their own main supplies or installations. The Clerk of Works is to see that the contractor affords all reasonable facilities to these authorities, and he should make note on his Weekly Report when they are working on site.

7 Work by Outside Specialists

In certain cases the Council gives permission to outside specialists for work, such as the installation of a radio relay system, to be carried out during the progress of the contract. Care must be taken by the Clerk of Works that these classes of operations do not involve excessive cutting away with consequent making good, and if in his opinion this occurs he should report to the architect-in-charge accordingly.

8 Labour-only Sub-contractor

Labour-only sub-contracting has become a most important feature of building contracting of late years, so much so in fact that sometimes a very small nucleus of key men directly employed by the main contractor are his only personnel on the site, all labour operations being sub-contracted—mostly on a labour-only basis. As the system develops main contractors will develop the management skills to operate this type of sub-contracting more efficiently. There are numerous labour-only gangs forming, and reforming, some establishing themselves and some dropping out. Added to which some parts of the industry are very much against the system and are working for the abolition of labour only generally. While a serious shortage of skilled labour exists labour-only subcontracting is likely to continue. The Clerk of Works should treat these labour-only sub-contractors, as any other sub-contractor, and should note their names on the Weekly Report, as requiring contractual approval in the usual way.

20 Materials

1 Material Approvals

Where materials are specified as ' equal to . . . or other approved ' and in other cases where so instructed by the architect-in-charge, the contractor will put up samples for approval. No decision is to be given by the Clerk of Works on these samples, which are to be referred to the architect-in-charge for his approval or otherwise. The Clerk of Works should note the approval or rejection in his site diary.

Any subsequent variation in the quality of these materials or any specific falling off from the standards required by the specification of any materials should be reported to the architect-in-charge. The Clerk of Works should note the variation from standard in his diary and in the Weekly Report.

Representative samples of approved articles such as ironmongery should be held in the Clerk of Works' office A full range of samples of all materials used on a contract is maintained in the Materials Section which the Clerk of Works should visit on occasion to keep himself fully informed.

2 Major Deliveries

Major deliveries including bulk deliveries of reinforcing steel should be notified in the Weekly Report.

3 Sources of Materials

The Council has to be satisfied as to the origin of a material as well as its apparent quality, and it may sometimes be necessary to call for certificates of origin. The Clerk of Works is to notify the architect-in-charge of any delivery to the contract that contains material of doubtful origin.

In cases where the contract requires material to be supplied from a particular source, the Clerk of Works is to give special attention to each delivery of materials to ensure that these conform to requirements.

In the case of timber care should be taken that timber including plywood, bears the markings that may be required in the specification. In the case of steel or steelwork the rolling marks and origin should be as required in the specification.

4 Deliveries of joinery

Good joinery timber is in short supply, and of necessity therefore we have to take more and more care that the parcels of joinery we receive in the deliveries to site fully meet the specification.

As soon as a joinery delivery is notified therefore arrangements should be made to have a specialist joinery team alerted to be ready for a detailed inspection, and a standard Joinery Inspection Report completed for the architect-in-charge.

Full details of the procedures to be adopted in this matter are contained in the section entitled JOINERY of this Handbook. These procedures should be strictly followed.

5 Direct Supply— Procedure

The Council arranges the supply and delivery direct to the site of certain articles under the Council's bulk purchase and Direct Supply scheme. The complete procedure for the supply and delivery of these articles is detailed in the specification or contract bills; and the Clerk of Works is to familiarise himself thoroughly with this procedure.

6 Direct Supply— Requisitioning

Requisition forms for articles supplied are given to the contractor normally with the Order to Commence, and he is required to complete and forward the requisitions to the Council in duplicate within a specified time. The Clerk of Works is to see that the contractor has the required forms and deals with them promptly; guidance should be given by the Clerk of Works to the contractor's Agent in this matter if necessary. Copies of the requisitions should be kept by the Clerk of Works for reference.

It is particularly important to order samples of articles when such are particularly useful—the contractor sometimes omits this.

7 Direct Supply— Deliveries

On receipt of articles supplied direct the contractor is responsible for detailed examination and check, and for the completion and disposal of signed Goods Received sheets in accordance with the terms of the specification. The Clerk of Works should make it his business to ensure that the contractor is fully aware of his responsibilities and knows that breakages, shortages, or quality deficiencies should be notified on Goods Received sheets in the manner, and within the time limit laid down.

8 Direct Supply—Quality

In the event of there being a doubt as to the quality of articles supplied direct, the Clerk of Works is immediately to notify the architect-in-charge who will arrange for an examination of the articles in question. Acceptance by the contractor of delivery of any articles is by no means deemed to constitute automatic approval of the article by the architect-in-charge; the latter will make arrangements for the inspection and approval of the first delivery of the articles or for a sample of each class of article. The Clerk of Works is to notify the architect-in-charge of the first deliveries of each type of bulk purchase direct supply article, so that arrangements for inspection can be made, if the architect-in-charge so desires. Thereafter the responsibility that the quantity and quality of the articles is correct rests primarily with the contractor.

9	**Direct Supply—Replacement**	Any replacements required by the contractor, for articles broken, damaged, or lost, after delivery must be requisitioned by the contractor on the usual form. As sometimes the few articles missing towards the end of a contract cause a delay out of all proportion to their value, the Clerk of Works can most usefully check that the contractor orders any necessary replacements sufficiently early to avoid delay in the work.
10	**Direct Supply—Delivery Delays**	The Clerk of Works is to make particular note of the delivery dates required by the contractor on his requisitions for all articles supplied direct. These dates should be forward-noted in the Clerk of Works' diary, and any delay in delivery of these articles should be brought to the attention of the architect-in-charge and noted in the regular Weekly Report.
		It is also necessary for the Clerk of Works to ensure that direct supply materials are not delivered too far ahead of site requirements. Where necessary the contractor should submit revised delivery schedules.
		It is not sufficient for the Clerk of Works to wait until the contractor is ready to use the articles in the work before notification of delivery delay is made, even although the contractor's Agent may have left the matter until the last moment.
		In the case of delivery delay difficulties the officer in charge of Direct Supply arrangements at the Materials Section is most invaluable, and in fact early liaison with this officer in the general Direct Supply procedure would be most advantageous.
11	**Name Plates**	Name and Indicator plates should be received by the Clerk of Works and checked for quantity, quality, and correctness of lettering and figures. The Clerk of Works should notify the architect-in-charge immediately of any discrepancies. The plates should then be handed to the contractor for use in the work and for the issue of Goods Received sheets in the usual way. Particular care is required in fixing enamelled plates that crazing does not occur at screw holes.
12	**Standardisation of Direct Supply Materials**	It is the intention that the pattern of Direct Supply articles and materials be standardised. If materials delivered by a supplier show a departure from standard the architect-in-charge is to be informed and his instructions sought.
13	**Damage to Baths**	Most of the damage to baths on sites is undoubtedly occasioned by the contractor's failure to properly protect the baths after installation, and a lot of this is impact damage.

Contractors argue constantly that either the damage is too trivial to bother about, or it was caused by a latent manufacturing defect, or it can be readily repaired, and in fact repairmen are sometimes brought on to a site to repair baths without the Clerk of Works being aware of it. If this question arises the Clerk of Works should inform the contractor's Agent that repairs are not accepted anywhere in the body of the bath, and that baths will not be accepted at handover if such repairs are attempted.

The officer in charge of Direct Supply arrangements in the Materials Section should then be called in to examine the question of triviality of defect or latent manufacturing defects. He is skilled in these matters and can offer great assistance to the site Clerk of Works. It should be noted that a number of these so called specialist repairs or 'touch-ups' are simply temporary and the fault discovers itself under use. The Clerk of Works should therefore maintain the attitude that all damaged baths to whatever degree must be rejected unless the architect-in-charge, advised by the Materials Section, or if necessary the Scientific Adviser, permits otherwise.

14 Prevention of Impact Damage

As impact damage is usually caused by other trades, and very often by the plasterer it should be the endeavour to have the plastering, and his clearing up operation completed before installing the bath.

15 Pads for Feet of Baths

It has been found necessary in the past, to reject a number of cast-iron baths owing to defects occurring in the glazing. Recent investigations have revealed that these defects might, at least in part, have been caused by undue strain and vibration on the foot lugs and the body of the bath at the points of attachment of the four feet when the bath is pushed into position (an operation normally found necessary owing to restricted space in the bathroom). In order to minimise these effects, it has been arranged that deliveries of each of the makes of low bath currently being supplied for use on new housing work will be delivered with four rubber pads for fitting on site between the four feet and the body of the bath to serve as a form of shock-absorber. The operation is quite simple and involves only the placing of a pad over each of the four foot lugs prior to bolting on the feet.

21 Testing

1 General policy on Testing

Tests on building materials and on parts of the work are necessary to ensure compliance with the contract requirements and to maintain throughout the contract the required quality of materials and workmanship. Any and every material used in building can be subjected to a test. If there is any doubt in a Clerk of Works' mind on any material, or mixture of materials, reference should be made to the architect-in-charge who will instruct as to whether a test is necessary, and the procedure that is to be adopted.

It is necessary that a prescribed minimum amount of testing be carried out. The Clerk of Works is responsible for ensuring that this testing is carried out, and that all tests are made in good and sufficient time to conform to the progress requirements of the contract.

2 Site Testing equipment

For tests on site the supply of equipment will normally be provided for in the contract and will be the contractor's responsibility. The Clerk of Works should ensure that this equipment is adequate and in first class order.

3 Laboratories at County Hall

1 The Testing Station (Room B35) in the Department of Planning and Transportation is very well equipped indeed to carry out strength determinations on structural materials, e.g., tests on concrete cubes, bricks, steel. etc. ; is well informed on the abilities and efficiency of the various ready mix concrete depots throughout London and will advise on the approval of such depots ; can test soil samples where urgently required ; and can advise on sampling methods where necessary including visiting sites where required.

2 The Scientific Branch in the Director-General's Department is similarly well equipped to carry out investigations, analyses and tests of all types of building materials and components, including paints and will advise as necessary including visiting sites as required.

4 Testing of Mastic Asphalt—Outside Laboratories

Where a Clerk of Works has reason to believe that asphalt material does not conform to specification or has trouble of any sort with asphalt either workmanship or material he should call on the services of an asphalt specialist from the Sites Manager's office who will visit the site and advise.

When samples are to be taken of mastic asphalt—

1 *From material in block form as delivered:* pieces to a total weight of not less than 3 kg are to be taken in approximately equal amounts from not less than 6 blocks selected at random.

2 *From a mixer or pot at time of laying:* a Sample 300 mm × 300 mm × 25 mm thick to be cast in a prepared wooden mould.

3 *After laying:* A Sample, not less than 300 mm×
300 mm and to full depth of material as laid. The
application of heat around the edges of the area to
be sampled is permissible; and the sample should be
taken by an asphalter.
When analysis is required this will be done by either of
the outside laboratories, Messrs Sandberg or Messrs
Harry Stanger who will report back to the officer named
on the Form AR. 77 (normally the Job Architect) which
form should accompany the samples.
Copies of the report are to be distributed to—
1 Main Contractor
2 Clerk of Works
3 Sites Manager AR/HO/C/SM
4 Materials Architect
5 Section file.

5 **Forms to accompany
samples**

The following forms, a specimen of each of which is
attached, are to be used as indicated:
1 *Sample Note and Report TS1:*
To accompany all test cubes or samples sent to the
Testing Station. The appropriate sizes of samples.
and relevant British Standards are listed on the
back of this form.
2 *Form SB/G6*
To accompany samples for Scientific Branch,
including paint samples.
3 *Form AR/23*
This is a wrap-around label to affix on tin containing
paint samples for laboratory analysis by Scientific
Branch.
4 *Form AR. 77 for asphalt samples:*
To accompany all bituminous samples requiring
specific laboratory analysis; this analysis will be
carried out by an outside laboratory.

6 **Supervision of
Sampling**

The Clerk of Works should supervise all sampling and
should allot a serial number to each sample for its
identification.
It is most important that all the information required by
the form to accompany the sample is given. In particular
the name and telephone number of the Clerk of Works
must appear on any form which he sends in; and if the
tests required are to establish compliance with either the
contract documents, or a By-law, or a British Standard,
the appropriate requirement should be given.

7 **Clerk of Works
Records**

All tests carried out on site are to be methodically
recorded in the Clerk of Works diary with their results.
And for tests off site, whenever materials are sent for test
(properly packed and labelled, and accompanied by the

appropriate form properly completed) a diary record is to be made. The result of the test when it is received should also be entered in the diary.

The Weekly Report should contain a note of:
1 Tests carried out on site and their results.
2 Materials sent off site for test.
3 Results of laboratory tests.

8 Tests on Site

There is not much of a dividing line as far as the Clerk of Works is concerned between the tests usually carried out on sites, inspections on site, and accuracy measurement checks on sites.

The more specific of these which could be listed as tests on site are as follows:
1 Examination of sand for cleanliness—by hand, and by field settling test.
2 Slump tests.
3 Covermeter checks. (See Section 10.42.)
4 Moisture content checks, e.g., of joinery.
5 Accuracy measurement checks.
6 Flue tests (copy of form for record, attached).
7 Drain tests
8 Paint dilution test by instant paint test method.
9 Field weight tests on lightweight screeds.

9 Samples sent from the site by Clerks of Works for test

The usually required off-site testing is as follows:
1 Aggregate, coarse and fine, grading analyses.
2 Cement testing—manufacturer's certificate usually accepted.
3 Mortar testing.
4 Concrete cube tests.
5 Concrete mix composition—analyses.
6 Paint—for laboratory test.
7 Bricks—strength, dimensions, and, if required, porosity.
8 Reinforcement—if of doubtful origin.
9 Precast concrete components, including paving slabs.
10 Timber window—random selection for breakdown examination.
11 Dampcourse material.

10 Testing schedule

At the beginning of the contract the Clerk of Works should discuss with the Job Architect the general scheme of testing that is to be carried out on the contract, particularly if there are any special materials or components requiring special attention and which the Clerk of Works may need to be briefed upon.

Wherever and whenever during the course of the contract the Clerk of Works has doubts about any material or component, other than those that are covered by the

normal testing, he should discuss with the Job
Architect and suggest appropriate testing.

11 Examination of sand

Sand is used in many places and many trades on sites
and it is always appropriate for the Clerk of Works to be
able to check on its cleanliness and silt content, in a
simple direct way.
If the usual hand test, i.e., rubbing some sand between
the hands, shows staining, the sand will be suspect and
the Clerk of Works should carry out a silt test as follows:
Fill a 200 c.c. measuring jar to 100 c.c. mark with sand,
add salt water (one teaspoon of salt per pint of water)
to the 150 c.c. mark, shake vigorously and leave to
settle for three hours, when there should not be more
than a 6 c.c. layer of silt (i.e., 6 per cent.) on top. If
there is more, a laboratory test should be made.
If there is 10 c.c. or more of silt the sand should be
rejected out of hand.
Where a measuring jar is not available a clear glass bottle
or jar will suffice; put in 65 mm of loose sand, make up
to 90 mm with salt water, shake, settle for three hours
when the silt layer must not be more than 5 mm.

12 Marine aggregates

Aggregates from marine sources shall be used only with
the prior approval of the architect.
When ready-mix marine aggregate concrete is being used
on site, the Clerk of Works should make arrangements
to visit the concrete supplier's depot and supervise the
taking of samples of marine aggregates (both fine and
coarse) for submission to the Testing Station at
County Hall.
When marine aggregates are supplied direct to the site,
similar sampling should be carried out.
The frequency of sampling should be agreed with the
architect, the structural engineer and the officer-in-
charge of the Testing Station.

13 Slump tests

The slump test on concrete is one of the most important
to carry out, and to record. The Clerk of Works should
note that this is to be carried out correctly by the ganger
or chargehand demonstrating the slump, in accordance
with the laid-down drill. (Full details for carrying out the
drill for this test are contained in the document given on
permanent issue to each Clerk of Works.)
The practical value of a slump test is as a control check
that no material change has been made in the water
content or mix proportions of a concrete mix from those
of the mix approved for the work at the beginning of the
concreting operation.
At the beginning of each day's concreting operation the
Clerk of Works is to determine the slump of the approved

mix proportioned as per specification, with correct water content to give a workability suitable to the position in which the concrete is being placed. Thereafter on that day for the same materials and the same or similar concrete placing operations the slump should remain the same, and should be checked by the Clerk of Works at least once in the morning and once in the afternoon or whenever the concrete might appear to be varying. A slump test is also to be carried out at the time concrete cube samples are taken, and is to be carried out at each delivery of ready-mixed concrete.

All results are to be recorded in the Clerk of Works diary, and a shear slump is to be noted as such.

14 Field weight tests on lightweight screeds

The weight per cubic foot is the most important control factor for a lightweight roof screed and it is important that this be known while the sub-contractor laying the screed is still on the site. For this reason the Clerk of Works is to take a cube from the lightweight screed at an early stage, weigh it at 24 hours old, to the nearest ounce, calculate the density in lb. per cubic foot, check this against contract requirements and notify this figure on his Weekly Report.

15 General remarks on drainage testing

Drains are to be tested by the contractor, who will provide all testing apparatus, in the presence of the Clerk of Works and the Public Health Inspector who must both be satisfied that the drains pass all tests demanded by the Local Authority.

Drainpipes should be water-tested from manhole to manhole at a test pressure of 1500 mm head of water at the highest point of a section under test, and the water pressure must be maintained for not less than ten minutes. Tests should be applied before the pipes are haunched with concrete or covered in, and repeated after backfilling the trench or heading.

Subsidence of test water may be due to one or more of the following causes:

1 Absorption by pipes and joints.
2 Sweating of pipes or joints.
3 Leakage at joints or from defective pipes.
4 Trapped air.

Allowance should be made for absorption by adding water until absorption has ceased when the test proper should commence.

Any leakage will be visible and the defective part should be cut out and made good. A slight amount of sweating, which is uniform, may be overlooked, but excessive sweating from a particular pipe or joint should be watched for and taken as indicating a defect to be made good. Except where a test is specified it will be usual to test any surface water drains that may be constructed of 'seconds' by simply filling the drain with water and noting that all joints are sound and that no pipes are fractured. The stringency of the test required will usually be determined by Local Authority requirements.

Tests by ball or mirror and lamp for straightness and obstruction may be required by the Local Authority and should be applied where possible.

Testing by smoke is not adequate for underground drainage.

Manholes should be tested for water tightness by filling them with water and observing any subsidence of water level.

The Clerk of Works is to record in detail in his diary all tests of drains during construction and at the completion of the contract.

Before completion of a contract the Clerk of Works is to ensure by rodding that all drains are clear and free from obstructions and all drains are to be tested for soundness immediately prior to handing over.

16 Pile Tests note

Selected piles will normally be load tested under instructions from the Structural Engineer, and in accordance with the piling specification, and the requirements of the District Surveyor. The piling contractor will carry out the test and the Clerk of Works is to make note that the tests have been carried out, in his Weekly Report and in his Special Pile Driving Record.

17 General remarks on paint testing

As additional to the 'Instant Paint Testing' for dilution referred to in the section on DECORATION, and in addition to sampling work undertaken as occasion demands by the Scientific Branch by direct site sampling, or through the Paint Inspector, the Clerk of Works must carry out his own full programme of sampling of paints in accordance with his instructions from the architect-in-charge.

At delivery of paint, and on confirmatory instruction from the architect-in-charge, the Clerk of Works is personally to send up for test a sample direct from the manufacturer's tins of each type of paint; primer, undercoat, and finishing coat. Each separate batch of paint is to be tested, i.e., each delivery bearing a different batch number. Batch numbers are marked on the bottom of the cans.

During the course of the work, at least twice as a routine, and on any occasion when the quality of the paint being applied is at all in question, the Clerk of Works is personally to take, and send up for test, samples of each type direct from the painters' kettles.

When taking a sample for laboratory examination it is

essential to stir the paint thoroughly and nearly to fill
the sample tin. The lid of the sample tin should be
replaced without delay and the tin shaken. Standard
labels are available and on them all the information
required (including the brand name in full detail) should
be entered. Samples of both undercoat and finish should
be submitted. Should a sample be found unsatisfactory
on laboratory examination, it will normally be required
that an unopened can be submitted for checking
purposes. Paint samples are to be forwarded to the
Chemist-in-Chief, Room 621A, Main Block, The County
Hall, in a perfectly clean container filled within 3 mm of
the top, adequately labelled, and with the lid firmly
fixed, and accompanied by Form SB.96 properly
completed by the Clerk of Works.
If upon examination difficulty is found in stirring any
paint delivered to the site the Clerk of Works should
report to the architect-in-charge immediately.
It should be noted by the Clerk of Works that no addition
except by the paint manufacturer, of thinners, driers or
other materials is permitted, and that therefore site
additions or dilutions by the contractor are expressly
forbidden.
The BS covering the paint, as stated in the specification,
is to be noted by the Clerk of Works on Form SB.96
accompanying the sample.

18 Tests on flues

All flues are to be tested by the contractor in the presence
of the Clerk of Works who is to note the test in his diary
and forward a certificate to the department at the
completion of each portion of the work, that the flues
have been tested in accordance with the specification
and found clear.

19 Testing of bricks

Special load-bearing bricks will be tested. Facing bricks
may require to be tested for porosity, and instructions
accordingly will be issued by the architect-in-charge.
Sample bricks should be taken from a stack or sample
load by moving the top two courses in the stack to open
a 'trench' enabling bricks to be taken from the third
and fourth courses below the top. For the initial test
figures 15 bricks will be taken at regular intervals from
the third and fourth courses and from each side of the
stack. The Clerk of Works is personally to see that the 15
bricks are taken as indicated and forwarded to the Council
Testing Station, accompanied by Form TS/1 properly
completed and giving the required crushing strength
where applicable, against the item 'purpose for which
materials are to be used'.
Subsequent check tests should be arranged on bricks
each time bricks from a new firing are delivered to the

site, or if it is noticed that there is any variation in texture, colour, soundness, or weight, in any of the deliveries.

20 Testing of slates

When slates require testing, on instructions from the architect-in-charge, the Clerk of Works is to arrange for six to be forwarded to the Council Testing Station accompanied by Form TS/1 properly completed, giving a precise description of the test required. In the case of dampcourse slates absorption, crushing, and density tests are required; and in the case of roofing slates absorption and density tests are required. In the latter case the pitch of the roof is to be stated.

21 Cement testing

Routine tests on every consignment are not normally necessary. If special circumstances, such as site deterioration, make testing desirable, then the Clerk of Works is to notify the architect-in-charge accordingly, and make arrangements for test.
Otherwise the architect-in-charge will issue instructions for the testing of cement during the course of the contract. For testing, a 5.0 kg sample should be to be dispatched to the Council Testing Station in an airtight tin; the cement should be well shaken down, the tin completely filled, and the lid sealed down by adhesive manila paper, labelled, dated, and signed by the Clerk of Works. Form TS/1 properly completed by the Clerk of Works is to accompany the sample.
Tins and manila tape will be supplied by the Department.

22 Testing of reinforcement

Steel either for reinforcement or otherwise, particularly steel of doubtful origin, may be subjected to test on instruction from the architect-in-charge in consultation with the structural or consulting engineer, if so required. When such tests are required, the architect-in-charge will say what samples are required and give instructions for delivery to GLC Testing Station. Samples should be accompanied by form TS/1, on the reverse side of which is given the size of samples, etc., to be taken.

GLC Testing Station and Soil Mechanics Laboratory
SAMPLE NOTE and REPORT   Form TS1

Send a separate form with each sample
Do not use parts edged red*

Sample number
Date received

Quantity

Name of Works   Works officer   telephone

Department   Branch   Surveyor's district

SAMPLING Proper sampling is essential for reliable testing
Record method used to obtain this sample by entering name of sampler in appropriate box (1) or (2)

GLC standard method (overleaf)	1
Alternative method (describe)	2

CONCRETE Position in Works

Mix   Aggregate size   Measured slump

Readymix company and plant   Cement content declared

Date cast   Cube size   Works sample mark

Test requirements			Test results			Test Notes
Cube	Test age	Strength required	Test date	Test age	Strength MN per sq.m	
A						
B						
C						
D						
E						
F						

OTHER MATERIAL and SOIL Position in Works

Description   Supplier   Specification
                                        B.S.
Date cast   G.L.C.
Tests required   Works sample mark

TEST REPORT

Report is sent to Department, copy to District Surveyor
Detailed results can be reported, on request   Officer in Charge

* Indicated here by a broken line.

107

GLC Testing Station and Soil Mechanics Laboratory
Room B35 The County Hall London SE1 7PB telephone 01-633 6195
GLC STANDARD SAMPLING METHODS FOR CONSTRUCTION MATERIALS

CONCRETE

SAMPLING	CUBE MAKING
Sampling—During discharge of a load from mixer or truck take a sample of at least 50 kg.	Cube making—Fill the 150 mm mould in three layers, tamp each layer at least 35 times with a steel rammer 38 cm long, 25 mm square, alternatively vibrate. Seal top of wet cube with plastic.
Fill buckets at ¼, ½, ¾ and ⅘ of discharge. Place the bucket to collect the whole stream. Alternatively use a scoop.	Store at 20°C for 1 day.
Combine the four portions and well mix.	Demould and send to Testing Station.
	Keep cube wet.

OTHER MATERIAL

AGGREGATE
From a load of not more than 10 tonne take a sample of at least 25 kg of coarse aggregate or 13 kg of fine aggregate. Take 10 portions from different parts of the load and combine to form the sample.

BRICK	BLOCK
From a load of not more than 10,000 bricks take a sample of 20 bricks. Divide the load into 10 equal parts and take 2 bricks from each part.	From a load of not more than 1000 blocks take a sample of 20 blocks. Divide the load into 10 equal parts and take 2 blocks from each part. Avoid taking blocks from the weathered outside of a stack.

FLAG	KERB
From not more than 2000 flags take a sample of 3 flags. Take each flag from a different part of the stack. Record cast date on Sample Note.	From not more than 1000 m run take a sample of 3 kerbs. Take each kerb from a different part of the stack. Record cast date on Sample Note.

BAR	ROAD ASPHALT
From not more than 45 tonne take at random 5 bars. From each bar cut a specimen 60 cm long.	From a load of not more than 20 tonne take a sample of at least 25 kg. Allow lorry to discharge half its load into the paver hopper, then back off. Take 6 portions from the face of the asphalt in the hopper and combine the portions. Send all the sample for test.

If larger samples are required take more portions or units.
Consult the Testing Station about methods of sampling soil and materials not here described.

(P.8383)

Greater London Council

SAMPLES FOR EXAMINATION

SB/G6

To: **The Scientific Adviser,**
   Scientific Branch,
   Room 621A, County Hall, S.E.I.
   (01-633 6280)

This form to be used for submission of samples requiring
either (*a*) Chemical analysis or evaluation.
or (*b*) Physical testing of properties such as acoustic and
   thermal conductivity, porosity and permeability,
   light-fastness, combustibility and flammability,
   heat and water-resistance.
or (*c*) Investigation of any apparent defects on site.

Sample(s) submitted by—Department ....

Section ....

Site ....

Description of Sample(s) ....

....

....

....

Manufacturer ....

Brand ....

Contractor ....

Specification requirements ....
   (If any)

....

Information required ....

....

Name of officer requiring report .... Telephone No. ....

FOR OFFICE USE

Signature of officer submitting sample ....

Date ....

Lab. Nos. ....

150 pads (TJ 23703-K46000) 7.72

AR23	GREATER LONDON COUNCIL—INNER LONDON EDUCATION AUTHORITY

FILL TIN 7/8 FULL   Paint Sample   **FILL TIN 7/8 FULL**

Department ....   Date ....

Premises or site ....   Contractor ....

Sample ref. no. ....   Painting Sub-contractor ....

Type of paint .... primer*/undercoat*/ finishing*

.... Interior*/Exterior*   Maker's Name ....

Brand ....   Maker's Batch No. ....

Colour ....   Sample from freshly opened can*/painter's kettle*

Sign GLC/ILEA rep: ....   Sign Contractor's rep: ....

*Strike out what is not applic bie

5m (W.A.S. 26372 B9947) 6/68

109

GREATER LONDON COUNCIL   AR.77

Department of Architecture and Civic Design

BITUMINOUS SAMPLES FOR ANALYSIS

TESTING LABORATORY

To: ....

....

(Insert name and address of laboratory)

This form to be used for the
submission of samples requiring
analysis or evaluation.

WORKS   Site/Contract...

Branch/Division...

SAMPLE(S)	Sample No.	Sample No.
1 Description		
2 Samples a) As delivered b) During laying c) After laying		
3 Where taken (location if 2c applies)		
4 Date of sampling		
5 Marking on samples (if any)		
6 Material specification		
7 Test(s) required†		
8 Additional information		

9 Samples submitted by ....*(Clerk of Works or other officer)*

Charge for testing to be invoiced to‡ ....

....

Report of analytical results to be sent to:

The Department of Architecture and Civic Design
Greater London Council   Attention of * ....
County Hall
London, SE1 7PB   ....
                                (Branch/Division)

---

† Whilst specific tests can be ordered if requested by the architect or specialist adviser, the normal tests would be:
For mastic asphalt – analysis and hardness number (according to appropriate BS)
For rolled asphalt and coated macadam – binder content, proportions, and classification of coarse aggregate

‡ If the samples are taken from a running contract the contractor's name and address should be inserted;
otherwise the charge should be invoiced to the Department of Architecture and Civic Design.

* Insert name and official address of job architect.

5m (SWP 16652 – B42103) 2.72.

22 Industrialised Buildings

1 General

A number of industrialised building methods or systems have been used by the Greater London Council, and a Clerk of Works must hold himself ready to supervise this type of work as well as traditional work.
A considerable number of blocks of dwellings have been built by industrialised methods, and considerable development was in hand in the mid-sixties when, understandably the Ronan Point disaster of 16 May 1968 caused a considerable check and general slowing down to this type of development. The disaster at Ronan Point designed on the Larsen Nielsen system, was triggered off by a domestic gas explosion on the eighteenth floor and involved the progressive collapse of part of a multi-storey block of flats, with some loss of life. An official enquiry reported with recommendations in October 1968 and was followed by numerous searching technical analyses of design and construction methods, and later a considerable programme of re-design, and remedial and strengthening works to all existing similar blocks.

2 Industrialisation

Industrialised building can broadly be defined as building construction using large factory-produced and finished panel units, usually of reinforced concrete, the basic construction method on site being erection or assembly rather than building. The term 'industrialisation' covers design factory manufacture, co-ordinated deliveries and erection to precise programmes.
There is constant development taking place in industrialised building, and the trend appears to be towards:
1 Increasing sophistication of methods of production for panel units.
2 The maximum of finish being applied at the factory.
3 Increasing production accuracy.
4 An improvement in the quality of workmanship as an automatic consequence of the increase in production accuracy; a matter of considerable importance to the Clerk of Works.
There are very many industrialised building 'systems' in the industry, varying from systems based on highly mechanised, large, permanent factories through site factories to systems which are simply a rationalisation of the normal building method.
The inspection requirements and methods of the Clerk of Works will vary to some extent depending on the method of production and the type of factory.

3 Tolerances

The Clerk of Works must make himself aware of the manufacturing and erection tolerances relating to his site, so that in case of any difficulty he is capable of checking in detail the appropriate dimensions of the particular component under examination.

4 Making good

The engineering specification will set out in detail principles for the acceptance or rejection of panel units or other components that have suffered damage, e.g., damage to a joint edge. It will also indicate whether in fact making good may take place on site or not, and give some measure of the allowable amount of such making good. The Clerk of Works should ensure that he is in possession of this type of specification, and if not should refer to the architect-in-charge.

Any cracking that might occur in a panel unit either before or after erection, as distinct from minor edge, corner, or surface damage, must be regarded seriously and in each case the structural engineer's attention must be called to the matter, and the architect-in-charge informed.

The architectural specification will detail the surface finishes to units required, and in the matter of damage to these units will set the principles of acceptance, or otherwise, for such units, and indicate whether the surface finish may be repaired on the site or not. In any case of a quality imperfection reference should be made to the architect-in-charge. When repair on site is undertaken, it will be the responsibility of the Clerk of Works properly to assess whether the quality of the making-good is completely acceptable. If there is any doubt the Clerk of Works should bring the matter to the attention of the architect-in-charge upon his next visit to the site.

5 The Clerk of Works in future development

At all times it is necessary, and advisable, for Clerks of Works to keep themselves abreast of the latest modern developments, particularly at a time when the limited building labour force of the country is so heavily overloaded.

23 Training and the Supply of Technical Information to Clerks of Works

1 Assistants under training by Clerks of Works

It is necessary to see that newly joined junior Clerks of Works are not only familiar with GLC normal routine but are given early experience of all types of contract and appropriate technical training so that they may adequately and confidently supervise any and every operation. Senior Clerks of Works should have this in mind when instructing their junior assistants under training.

2 Training by experience—Clerks of Works—in course of duty

Normally the training of junior Clerk of Works acting as assistant will include all, or the majority of, the following:

1 Three months on a commencing contract with standard foundations.
2 Concrete course at Cement and Concrete Association, Wexham Springs.
3 Three months on a contract with piled foundations.
4 Short surveying refresher course.
5 Three months on a contract which has tall buildings in the structural stage.
6 Timber course at the Timber Research and Development Association laboratories.
7 Three months on finishes to buildings and handover of completed buildings.
8 Short course of lectures on paintwork and paint testing. These may be followed by a period on contracts involving one of the processes of industrialised building.

3 Study by Clerks of Works—for personal qualifications

The assistant under training will also be expected to follow a suitable course of study which will not only fit him completely for his job, but also lead to some qualification appropriate to the position of Clerk of Works, e.g., Ordinary National Certificate; Higher National Certificate (preceded usually by a General Construction Course); Construction Technicians Course; a course of studies leading to membership of the Institute of Builders or a course of study designed to qualify for membership of the Institute of Clerk of Works, by examination.

A suitable qualification appropriate to the position of Clerk of Works has become of increasing importance of late years in the industry as a whole and it may well be that established Clerks of Works may wish to avail themselves of the opportunities to study for such qualification.

Under certain circumstances time off for day studies may be granted by the Council, and it may also be possible for the expenses in connection with any approved course of study to be paid. Applications for day leaves or course payments should be made to the Establishment Officer giving all the necessary details of the studies to be undertaken, when the Establishment Officer will indicate whether day leaves or course payments are possible. Clerks of Works will need to make their own complete arrangements for these study courses leading to personal qualifications.

4 Courses for Clerks of Works arranged by the Department

It will be the normal procedure for each Clerk of Works in the Department, Senior and Junior, to take at some stage the following courses, with follow up courses as required. These will be arranged by the Department, and the Clerks of Works will attend under departmental instructions:

1 Concrete construction course for G.F.'s and Clerks of Works at the Cement and Concrete Association.
2 Short surveying refresher course.
3 Short theodolite course.
4 Timber course either at Timber Research and Development Association, or at the D of E. Princes Risborough Laboratory.
5 Short course on painting (Organised via Local School of Building and/or Technical Colleges).

It should be noted that when assigned to any course obligatory for the Clerk of Works to attend, and any absence, except by prior arrangement, has to be the subject of a note to the Establishment Officer.

5 Initial issues of technical information to Clerks of Works

Each Clerk of Works in charge of a contract will be issued with:

1 GLC Architects' Department Clerk of Works Handbook.
2 Permanent issue set of selected British Standards (as listed below).
3 Permanent issue set of selected Codes of Practice (as listed below).
4 Permanent issue set of Building Research Digests (as listed below).
5 London Building Acts Constructional By-laws with explanatory memorandum—applicable to the Inner London Boroughs.
6 The Building Regulations 1976, applicable to all areas of England and Wales except Inner London.
7 By-laws of the Metropolitan Water Board.
8 The Drainage By-laws, applicable to the Inner London Boroughs.
9 The Means of Escape Regulations applicable to the Inner London Boroughs.
10 Book of Standard Patterns for colour matching.
11 Set of 'Man on the job' pamphlets relating to concrete work in the field. (C. & C.A.)
12 Metric Information Handbook.

13 Concrete Practice Pt. I. Materials and Workmanship (C & CA).
14 Concrete Practice Pt. II. Site Supervision and Testing (C & CA).

6 Permanent issue Set of BRITISH STANDARDS for Clerks of Works

BS No	TITLE
65 and 540	Clay pipes and fittings
187 Pt 2	Sand lime bricks
340	Pre-cast concrete kerbs
416	Cast iron pipes
437 Pt 1	Cast iron pipes and fittings
455	Locks and latches
459 Pts 1-4	Wooden doors
460	Cast iron rain water goods
497	Manhole covers
539	Dimensions of fittings for clay drain pipes
585	Wood stairs
644 Pts 1-3	Wood windows
743	Materials for DPCs metric units
747 Pt 2	Roofing felts metric units
952	Glass
988 to 1451	Mastic asphalt for building
1186 Pts 1 and 2	Joinery 1. Quality of Timber. 2. Quality of Workmanship
1243	Metal ties
1297	Grading and sizing of Softwood flooring
1331	Builders hardware for housing
1567	Wood door frames and linings
1860	Structural timber
1881 Pts, 1, 2 3 and 6	Method of testing concrete
1926	Ready mixed concrete
3921 Pt 2	Standard special bricks
4408 pt 1	Cover tests on concrete
4408 pt 4	Surface hardness methods
4466	Bending dimensions and scheduling of bars
4471	Dimensions for softwood
4551	Testing mortar
4721	Ready-mixed lime: sand for mortar
4729	Shapes and dimensions of special bricks
PD 6440	Accuracy in Building (Metric Units)
BS 4978	Timber grades for structural use

7 Permanent Issue Set of CODES OF PRACTICE for Clerks of Works

CP No	TITLE
98	Preservative treatments for constructional timber
97 Pt 1	Common scaffolds in steel
101	Foundations and Substructures for non-industrial buildings of not more than four storeys

	102	Protection against ground water
	112	The structural use of timber
	121.101	Brickwork
	144 Pt 4	Mastic asphalt
	151	Wooden doors
	152	Glazing and fixing of glass for buildings
	153 Pt 2	Durability wood windows
	211	Internal Plastering
	231	Painting of buildings
	301 (1971)	Building drainage

		No.	**TITLE**
8	**Permanent Issue Set of**	3	Working in Winter or Bad Weather
	BRS DIGESTS for	6	Drainage for Housing
	Clerks of Works	8	Built up felt Roofs
		9	Dry-lined interiors to Dwellings
		13	Concrete Mix Proportioning and Control
		15	Pipes and Fittings for Domestic Water Supply
		21	New types of Paint
		27	Rising Damp in Walls
		32	Simplified Plumbing for Housing
		36	Jointing with Mastics and Gaskets—I
		37	Jointing with Mastics and Gaskets—II
		47	Granolithic Concrete, Concrete Tiles and Terrazzo Floors
		49	Choosing Specifications for Plastering
		51	Developments in Roofing
		53	Project Network Analysis
		54	Damp-Proofing Solid Floors
		55	Painting Walls I
		56	Painting Walls II
		57	Painting Walls III
		58	Mortar for Jointing
		59	Protection Against Corrosion of Reinforcing Steel
		63	Soils and Foundations—I
		64	Soils and Foundations—II
		65	The Selection of Clay Building Bricks—I
		66	The Selection of Clay Building Bricks—II
		67	Soils and Foundations—III
		70	Painting Metals in Buildings—I Iron and Steel
		71	Painting Metals in Buildings—II Non Ferrous Metals
		72	Home Grown Softwoods for Buildings
		73	Prevention of Decay in Window Joinery
		75	Cracking in Buildings
		77	Damp Proof Courses
		79	Clay Tile flooring
		80	Soil and Waste Pipe Systems for Housing

9 Periodical Information

Technical notes, instructions, addenda, and amendments will be issued from time to time for insertion in the Clerk of Works Handbook, and amendments and addenda will also be issued for the other documents held by Clerks of Works.

It is the Clerk of Works responsibility to see that these are kept up to date. It is not the intention to issue to Clerks of Works codes, standards or brochures which in the main are concerned with design, or any that are unnecessary for work on site, but there is a mass of information produced each year for the building industry, and if any Clerk of Works desires information on any special subject this can be produced by the Sites Managers office for loan to the Clerk of Works concerned.

10 Students and Trainee Attachments

At times a student or trainee may be attached to the office of a Clerk of Works on a Council site. The object is that the student or trainee should gain knowledge, or improve his existing knowledge, of practical building constructions. The Clerk of Works should do his best to assist towards this end.

Although the student or trainee can assume no official responsibility, an attachment is of much reduced value and interest when he does no work. The Clerk of Works in charge should therefore give the student specific jobs to do, some of which will be similar to those carried out by an assistant Clerk of Works. Students and trainees will be of variable ability and experience, and the jobs given should be within their competence.

11 Suitable jobs for students or trainees

Some maintain that the way to learn about building is to get behind the mixer with a shovel and similarly labour at other trades. This is considered wrong. A student in training should not waste time practising work that is carried out by operatives, nor attempt to learn a craftsman's skills. Suitable jobs where a student can with advantage participate, in short attachments to sites are:

1 Checking the contractors grid levels of a site.
2 Checking the contractors setting out of the main site and one or two individual blocks.
3 Study of the overall construction method—and this is probably the most important item of all.
4 Attendance at site meetings.
5 Accuracy check measurements of vital dimensions and tolerances.
6 Engaging in ' snagging ' which means the detailed examination of work to ascertain defects or omissions, and the assessment of quality.
7 Following up snagging to see how and what the contractor does to remedy errors.
8 Preparing progress statements for site meetings.

12 Planning useful attachments

A series of short planned visits to a site or sites are more advantageous to a student than long continuous a.m. to p.m. sessions for several weeks; and the architect-in-charge of the project, when being asked to agree to student attachments could well be asked whether he would be prepared to give guidance on the planning of a programme of visits to enable the student or students to gain the maximum advantage.
It may be appropriate that students should carry out attachments in pairs.

24 Relations with other Departments and Branches

1 General Co-ordination

The Clerk of Works is to see that officers of other departments and branches are afforded all necessary facilities to enable them to carry out their duties, and that there is proper and full co-ordination with these officers in all matters relating to the contract. The Clerk of Works should note in his diary and Weekly Report the visits of the officers concerned and any decisions that may have been taken affecting the works.

2 Structural Engineer

When the structural engineer inspects foundations or structural work, the Clerk of Works should see that the work is fully prepared beforehand for inspection, including ready means of access to deep foundations, and should attend on the structural engineer during his inspection.

If a Clerk of Works has "Designed-mix" concretes on his work then particularly close liaison with the structural engineer is necessary as records of control test cubes may be required for statistical control and it is probable that the structural engineer would appreciate the Clerk of Works assistance here.

Similarly where concrete is supplied by the ready mix method, even if not particularly designated as a designed mix, a tight control on the ready mix supply is necessary and a close liaison with the structural engineer is most appropriate. Additionally where a mix is specified as a nominal mix and is being produced on site, it must be proportioned by weight and the weight of the aggregates should be agreed with the structural engineer.

Reference should of course be made to the structural engineer in all cases where special measures for concreting in cold weather are to be used for structural work.

In the general matter of liaison with the structural engineer the Clerk of Works should see that he knows the section of this Handbook entitled 'Concrete and Reinforced concrete' as well as the detailed provisions of the specification.

3 Housing Engineer

An officer of the Housing Engineers division may carry out routine visits to inspect roads and sewer works on housing developments.

Any observations that may effect adjustments to the works should be noted for the information of the architect-in-charge; and the visiting officers advice sought on any matter that may assist the Clerk of Works.

4 Quantity Surveyor

The Clerk of Works is required to assist the Quantity Surveyor by obtaining and recording any particulars that officer may need in connection with valuations or adjustment of variations.

5   District Surveyor

The District Surveyor's organisation, a body of highly trained and skilled professional officers, believed to be without parallel in any other city in the world, has the task of ensuring that all building structures in the Inner London area, other than those specifically exempt and subject to other control, are built strictly in accordance with the London Building Act and By-Laws made in consequence of that Act.

The District Surveyor amongst other things:

1 Discusses preliminary building proposals with developers, including this Department.
2 Carries out surveys of dangerous structures and serves appropriate notices.
3 Examines structural calculations and design details of proposed developments.
4 Advises upon waivers; and
5 Inspects the construction work, including foundations, from time to time to check that all work subject to the London Building Act and By-Laws is carried out ' in a proper and workmanlike manner' to his satisfaction.

The District Surveyor has considerable powers. If a builder does work which is not in accordance with the Act and By-Laws then a District Surveyor can serve a 48-hour notice of what must be done to correct the work, and in the final analysis ask the Courts to fine the builder concerned.

6   Relationships between District Surveyor and Clerk of Works

It will be seen that the aims of the Clerk of Works and of the District Surveyor are coincidental in that they both want 'work carried out in a proper and workmanlike manner'. The Clerk of Works therefore has a very powerful ally and he should treat the District Surveyor as such.

It should be noted that the District Surveyor does not officially need to pass any instructions through the Clerk of Works, nor as far as the London Building Act is concerned need he inform him at all; the District Surveyor will instruct the builder direct, and may or may not contact the Clerk of Works.

Nevertheless the Clerk of Works must carefully attend on the District Surveyor or his deputy or assistant whenever any of these officers visit the site, and must make a note of any instructions any of these officers give to the builder, or to the Clerk of Works. The Clerk of Works should inform the architect-in-charge by telephone of any especially important instructions given, and also make the appropriate note in his diary.

| 7 | **Mutual Confidence between Clerk of Works and District Surveyor** | A feeling of mutual confidence between the District Surveyor and the Clerk of Works is a most valuable thing, and will make a good structural contract so much easier to achieve. It is essential, in the case of remedial measures or alterations affecting any interference whatsoever with structural work, that the District Surveyor be informed immediately the need for this work becomes apparent. |

This applies to all alterations or remedial works affecting structural work, including the cutting back of a 'proud' concrete face, cutting out of any honeycombed concrete, pulling down of faulty structural brickwork and similar measures. The architect-in-charge must also be made aware of such alterations or remedial works so that if he desires he may discuss the matter with the District Surveyor, or have the structural engineer do so, before the work is put in hand. Either way the Clerk of Works should be very sure that the District Surveyor is confident that he will be kept fully and immediately informed of all structural matters that occur on the contract. The Clerk of Works must ensure that such confidence is never misplaced.

| 8 | **Aesthetic considerations** | It might be noted that the District Surveyor's concern is for structural matters and he is not unduly concerned with aesthetics. The architect-in-charge has a large over-riding interest and concern in aesthetic as well as in structural matters and, naturally, the Clerk of Works has a similar concern in both fields. |

| 9 | **Public Health Inspector** | The Clerk of Works should record in his diary the date of the Public Health Inspector's visits for the purpose of testing sections of drainage, and the results of such tests. |

| 10 | **Electrical and Heating Inspectors** | The Clerk of Works should establish early liaison with the Electrical and Heating Inspectors so that the works of the relevant subcontractors are properly co-ordinated with the rest of the work on the contract, and all points of detail made clear to all concerned. Similar action should be taken, of course, for all other specialist services. |

| 11 | **Factory Inspector** | It is the duty of the Clerk of Works to report upon any plant or scaffolding in use, or intended to be used, which appears to be defective or dangerous. The report should be made to the Sites Manager's office so that the department's Chief Safety Officer may take the appropriate action. The Clerk of Works is also to note, in his Weekly Report, when a Factory Inspector visits his site, and any remarks he may make on safety matters. |

12 Officers of the Parks Department

Good liaison with the appropriate officer of the Parks Department should be established during the progress of the contract so that arrangements may be made for the completion of the planting work, as near as possible to coincide with the contract completion; and so that the Parks Department's Clerk of Works specialist skills are used to the full in assisting the Site Clerk of Works in obtaining a job that is first class in every way.

25 Clerks of Works Conditions of Service and General Administration

(These notes are intended as a guide to some of the more important of the Conditions of Service of a Clerk of Works. Engagements are subject to the Council's standing orders, regulations and rules in force from time to time; requests for advice on queries or difficulties should be made to the Establishment Officer.)

1 Hours of Work

The Clerk of Works is required to work the hours of the Contractor which, in the building industry at the moment, are 40 per week basic, and are worked in a five-day week:
  8 a.m.–12 noon
  1 p.m.–5 p.m. (or 4.30 p.m. in case of $\frac{1}{2}$-hour lunch).
During the winter period, six weeks before to six weeks after Christmas the Contractor may, if he so wishes, work the 40 hours basic in a five and a half day week, i.e., Monday to Thursday $7\frac{1}{4}$ hours each, Friday 7 hours, and Saturday 4 hours. The time allocated for lunch break is excluded in all cases. Punctual attendance in the morning is essential.

2 Overtime

Most contractors, except those engaged on maintenance work, do regular overtime.
Where the work being done during the overtime period cannot be properly inspected on the following day, the Clerk of Works will be required to work overtime, i.e. operations such as structural concrete work, removal of obstructions etc. The Clerk of Works will use his judgement to decide when the nature of the work makes it necessary for him to work overtime.
Overtime, each day, commences for a Clerk of Works after the basic eight hours have been worked, excluding the time the site allocates for the lunch interval.
If work is carried out on a Saturday on a site with a five-day week, a Clerk of Works' overtime will start from the beginning of the day's work, i.e. 8.00 a.m.

3 Overtime Claims

Overtime claims must be:
1 Submitted to the divisional administration on the first day of each month for overtime worked in the previous month showing details of overtime and weekly sub-totals of hours worked and
2 Endorsed ' Operatives on site worked similar overtime '.
  and signed by the Clerk of Works.
It should be noted that overtime spent on clerical work when operatives are not on site does not rank for payment.
All overtime hours which rank for payment should, of course, be shown on the weekly report as well as on the Overtime Claim.

123

4   Attendance Records   All Clerks of Works are to show their times of arrival and departure and their overtime hours on the Weekly Report form.
Additionally all Clerks of Works are to complete, and have in County Hall by 3 p.m. every Monday, a time analysis sheet AR 74A which sheets will be analysed by the County Hall computer for cost of production information.
To fill in this form each Clerk of Works will need to know:
1 his personal salary code number
2 his personal salary classification
3 the week number
4 the job computer reference number.
Each Clerk of Works is given an explanatory sheet as to how this time analysis sheet AR 74A for computer use is to be filled in.

5   Temporary Absence Sheets   Clerks of Works are to leave a note whenever they have to leave their base sites during working hours, stating destination, purpose of visit, time of leaving and time of returning to the site.
The approval of the architect-in-charge must be obtained before leaving the site.

6   Travel Expenses— Home to Site   Clerks of Works are in most cases eligible for the reimbursement of a proportion of their travel expenses between their home and their site. As an example, taking the case of a Clerk of Works living and working inside Greater London, his travelling expenses between home and site, return, in excess of 21p per day are reimbursed.

7   Incremental Scales   Within the incremental scales normal annual increments will be paid subject to a certificate by the head of the division that the conduct, work and general efficiency of the officer has been in all respects satisfactory. Individuals will not normally be advised of annual increments, nor will they necessarily be called for interview at the time an increment is due. If the head of a division considers, however, that a normal annual increase should be withheld a written report will be made on the reasons for this and shown to the officer concerned, who should initial as having seen it.

8   Established Positions   With very few exceptions Clerks of Works are first recruited as temporary Clerks of Works, and subject to adequate reports and medical examination, they are then moved on to the permanent establishment some twelve to eighteen months later.
Only very occasionally are Clerks of Works engaged on the basis of individual projects, except for the ' Painting and Cleaning ' Clerks of Works engaged seasonally.

| **9** | **Superannuation** | A superannuation contribution of 6% of salary for the GLC Pension Scheme is deducted from a Clerk of Works salary from the date of his first joining the Council as a temporary officer, unless his age is a bar. |

| **10** | **Place of Employment** | A Clerk of Works has to be prepared to work anywhere in the Greater London Area. Regard is however paid to where he lives as far as practicable.
When he is asked to work at some distance outside the Greater London area, he becomes eligible for subsistence allowance if the posting is for a limited duration, or special arrangements are explored. |

| **11** | **Training** | Where a Clerk of Works is in need of training, regard is paid to this in posting as far as it is possible to give the Clerk of Works adequate training by experience. Clerks of Works are regularly sent on courses, and study for appropriate qualifications is encouraged. Day release is possible for suitable Clerks of Works. |

| **12** | **Car Allowances** | When a Clerk of Works has to be mobile between contracts or in estate areas when public transport is inappropriate, a car allowance may be made available. At the moment this is usually 7.1p per mile for the first 3000 miles a year, reducing to 5.1p per mile for the next 4000 miles a year, and 4.1p a mile thereafter. Special application has to be made by the Clerk of Works for a car allowance and this is only granted where it is specifically in the Council's interest to do so. |

| **13** | **Leave** | The leave year is from 1 April-31 March.
Annual entitlement for all Clerks of Works (Grades 1 to 4) is:
    26 basic working days. |

| **14** | **Leave on building operatives' holidays** | All Clerks of Works may take the occasional special additional day's leave that occurs at some Christmases due to operatives' holidays.
Clerks of Works in post at 30 September 1972 are allowed to retain on a personal basis the entitlement to leave on days on which the works supervised are closed due to normal building operatives' holidays.
Clerks of Works not in post by that date will be redeployed from their existing sites to other work when affected by site closures due to normal building operatives holidays. |

| **15** | **Additional leave for long service** | With effect from April 1974 Clerks of Works are entitled to leave additional to the annual leave prescribed for |

125

their grades, based on length of service as follows:
After 10 years service—additional 1 day
After 15 years service—additional 2 days
After 20 years service—additional 3 days
After 25 years service—additional 4 days
After 30 years service—additional 5 days

16 Special Leave

There are provisions for petty leave, or special leave in appropriate circumstances, e.g., moving house, funeral of a near relative, or similar urgent private affairs. This is subject to application to the Establishment Officer.

17 Application for Leave

When a Clerk of Works is granted leave it will normally be necessary for his contract to be covered by another Clerk of Works. For this reason it is necessary that a Clerk of Works makes his leave application at least two clear weeks before leave is required. Longer notice is advisable.

18 Termination of Engagement

The engagement for an officer on salaried staff may be terminated by one calendar month's notice in writing on either side; or on the part of the Council by
1 Six weeks notice if the employee has ten years but less than fifteen years continuous service; or
2 Eight weeks notice if the employee has fifteen years or more continuous service.

19 Illness

If an officer is prevented by illness from attending for duty he must on the first day of absence notify the fact and give the reason, by telephone if possible, to the Establishment Officer, and in the case of the Housing Branch to the Site Manager's office. If the illness continues beyond three days a medical certificate must be sent on the fourth day stating the cause of the illness. Further certificates should be forwarded as necessary to cover the whole period of sickness. On resumption of duty after a period of certificated sick leave a certificate stating that the officer is fit for duty must be produced.

20 Accidents

Accidents to an officer on duty, however trivial they may appear at first, should be reported immediately to the Establishment Officer.

21 Sick Pay

Provided that the requirements as regards notification of illness and submission of medical certificates are complied with and subject to the Council's right to determine the contract of service at any time, the following scales of sick pay are allowed:

Year of Service	The scales for sick pay	
	Full Pay—followed by—Half Pay	
In first 4 months	1 month	Nil
In first year thereafter	1 month	2 months
In Second year	2 months	2 months
In Third year	4 months	4 months
In Fourth year	5 months	5 months
In Fifth year	5 months	5 months
After completing six years' service	6 months	6 months

22 Assessment Boards

Assessment boards are held departmentally at intervals. At these boards the Clerk of Works will usually be asked to describe in some detail the work upon which he is engaged, and he will also be given the opportunity to ask any questions affecting his work or his career that he may wish.

23 Loss of Council money or property

1 All losses of money or property of the Council, irrespective of the amounts or value are to be reported immediately to the Department. Losses include thefts, burglaries and deficiencies discovered on inventory checks.
The report (3 copies) should contain the following information:
(*a*) Date and time of loss and its discovery.
(*b*) Cause of the loss and the circumstances of its discovery.
(*c*) Value of the individual items concerned. Where the total value of the losses discovered on any particular inventory check total £25 or less and a detailed valuation would involve much work, a list of items and a statement that the total value of the items was £25 or under will be sufficient.
(*d*) Contractor's security arrangements.
(*e*) Whether the loss has been reported to the police.
2 The Department should also be informed of the recovery of any money or property reported lost.
3 In addition, any burglary on a site should be reported to the police immediately and the contractor asked to carry out works necessary to make the premises secure, without prior reference to head office.
4 Safeguarding of council property—cash, stamps, etc., should never be left in an exposed position in an unoccupied room, or hut, but should be locked away.

24 Personal property

Claims for the loss or damage of personal property should be addressed to the contractor and not form part of the claim made by the Council for the loss of Council property.

25 Change of Address

The Clerk of Works is to notify the department at once of any change of private address, or of telephone number.

26 Correspondence

All communications for the department are to be addressed to The Architect, Greater London Council, The County Hall, London, SE1. Separate communications are to be made with respect to each contract supervised but are as far as possible to be dispatched in one envelope. The appropriate divisional reference, followed by the Job No., should be written on the top left hand corner of the envelope as well as on the documents themselves.

On pressing matters the Clerk of Works should communicate with the department by telephone. Where call fees are incurred they are to be charged to petty cash.

Correspondence from departments will normally be addressed to the Clerk of Works at his office on site, and the Clerk of Works should inform the department of the full postal address of the site office as soon as it has been established, and his telephone number.

Weekly Reports and Labour Returns are to be posted to reach the department not later than 3.0 p.m. on the Monday of each week.

27 Postage

Requisitions for postage stamps should be made on Form AR.58. An account of requisitions should be kept; postage stamps are not to be charged to petty cash. Any unused stamps are to be returned to the Department when no longer required.

28 Visitors to the works

Persons other than officers of the department, or the contractor or his accredited agents, visiting the works and asking to be furnished with information or to see drawings, should be required to produce authorisation from the architect-in-charge before any such request is granted, or obtain authorisation from the architect-in-charge by telephone.

29 Photographs

Applicants for permission to take photographs on the works should be referred by telephone to the architect-in-charge.

30 Trade Union visitors

Personal or written applications to visit the site made by Trade Union officials should be referred to the contractor's Site Agent.

31 Enquiries for housing

Any enquirers for housing accommodation are to be

informed that all communications regarding lettings on the Council's estates should be addressed to the Director of Housing, either at The County Hall or at the nearest District Office.

The names of individual members of the staff must not be given to such enquirers.

32 Visits from the Press

In the case of Press visitors, the Clerk of Works is to remember that no communication of any information to which access is obtained in the course of official duties is to be made to any newspaper, or person.

Visitors from a newspaper should be referred to the Press Officer (of whom they will be aware) at County Hall; and the architect-in-charge should be informed, by telephone, of the visit.

33 Examination of materials in preparation off-site

The Clerk of Works may from time to time need to visit outside workshops or yards where materials are in preparation, and satisfy himself as to the quality of material and the workmanship during execution before the finished work is delivered to the site. Prior permission for such visits is to be obtained from the architect-in-charge.

With the above exceptions the Clerk of Works is not permitted to visit manufacturers' works or showrooms during site working hours.

34 Rules for visits by the Clerk of Works to Workshops

When Clerks of Works visit workshops on inspection duties the party should consist of never less than a team of two officers. They should proceed in either Council, public or their own transport, and meals or similar full refreshments are to be taken under the officers own arrangements only.

Arrangements should be made for the visiting officers to arrive at the works early in the day, normally not later than 9 a.m., and leave only when a satisfactory day's inspection has been carried out. In the case of the Housing Branch the Sites Manager's office will arrange transport when required and the site Clerk of Works should notify that office when visits to workshops are required.

35 Issues

A Clerk of Works (Housing Branch) is issued with the following on entering the service:

Donkey jacket
Rubber boots
Stockings
Max. and Min. Thermometer
Rubber torch
30 metre Steel Tape—Metric
2 metre folding rod—Metric

together with the permanent issue sets of technical information for Clerks of Works detailed in section 'TRAINING AND SUPPLY OF TECHNICAL INFORMATION TO CLERKS OF WORKS'. Application for any of these articles should be made to the Site Manager's office.

36 Use of official position

All departmental documents, plans, photographs, etc., are to be regarded as classified and are not to go out of the department, or to be used for other than official purposes without special permission.
No official is entitled to have access to any paper which is not required by him in connection with his official duties.

37 Gifts

The acceptance of gifts from contractors, or sub-contractors, or any of their employees is expressly forbidden.
It is quite common for gifts to be offered at Christmas time and should these be delivered to an officer in such a way that he is given no opportunity to refuse or return them he should send or take the gifts to the Establishment Officer who will arrange for them to be either delivered to one of the London hospitals or otherwise disposed of.